PUFFIN BOOKS
ICONS FROM THE WORLD OF SCIENCE

S. Ananthanarayanan has an MSc. in physics and after a series of jobs, including selling insulation contracts, a spell in a newspaper and some time in a bank, came to roost in the Indian Railways, where he works as financial adviser. He is married and has two children.

ICONS
FROM THE
WORLD OF SCIENCE

S. Ananthanarayanan

Portraits by Sujata Bansal
Other illustrations by the Author

PUFFIN BOOKS

PUFFIN BOOKS

Penguin Books India (P) Ltd., 11 Community Centre, Panchsheel Park,
New Delhi 110 017, India
Penguin Books Ltd., 80 Strand, London WC2R 0RL
Penguin Group Inc., 375 Hudson Street, New York, NY 10014, USA
Penguin Books Australia Ltd., 250 Camberwell Road, Camberwell,
Victoria 3124, Australia
Penguin Books Canada Ltd., 10 Alcorn Avenue, Suite 300, Toronto,
Ontario, M4V 3B2, Canada
Penguin Books (NZ) Ltd., Cnr Rosedale & Airborne Roads, Albany,
Auckland, New Zealand
Penguin Books (South Africa) (Pty) Ltd., 24 Sturdee Avenue, Rosebank
2196, South Africa

First published in Puffin by Penguin Books India 2004

Text and illustrations except portraits copyright © S. Ananthanarayanan 2004

Portraits copyright © Sujata Bansal 2004

10 9 8 7 6 5 4 3 2 1

Dedicated to my family

Typeset in Palatino by Eleven Arts, Delhi 35

Printed at Pauls Press, New Delhi

CONTENTS

Preface   vi

1. J.C. Bose   1

2. Srinivasa Ramanujan   13

3. C.V. Raman   27

4. S.N. Bose   41

5. Meghnad Saha   55

6. S. Chandrasekhar   69

7. Homi Bhabha   83

8. Hargobind Khorana   97

9. E.C. George Sudarshan   111

10. Jayant Narlikar   125

PREFACE

During the late nineteenth and early twentieth centuries, India surged into the modern world with scientific contributions of the highest importance in diverse fields. Today, this work is an integral part of our common scientific awareness but the individual contributions of the scientists are perhaps not so well known. The pages that follow are short accounts of the work of ten Indian scientists who rank among the most influential in their respective areas. It is striking that at a time when India was hardly developed in technology, the work done in science was at the frontiers of knowledge.

This book is the outcome of a desire to bring science to young and non-specialist readers.

J.C. BOSE

THE INVENTION THAT HAD THE GREATEST impact on developments in many spheres of life in the twentieth century is certainly wireless telegraphy, which made 'instant' communication across continents possible. The credit for the invention is generally given to Guglielmo Marconi, but more and more people are now accepting that Jagadish Chandra Bose had publicly demonstrated the basis of the same thing in 1896, a full two years before the Italian! And although Marconi went on to perfect wireless, Bose's research laid down the foundation of microwave communication, which is at the heart of more advanced telecommunications developed many years later.

Jagadish Chandra Bose was born in 1858, in Mymensingh, a quiet village in the then undivided state of Bengal. His early education was in a village school, in the Bengali language, followed by school and college at St. Xavier's College, Kolkata. University education in India was still in its infancy at the time. Colleges had started offering university courses only in the 1860s. When J.C. Bose took his BA in physical sciences in 1879, he may have been one of the first Indians to be trained in the European tradition. It is remarkable that in just a few years, Bose became one of the leaders in research in physics, made important discoveries and was elected as a member of the Royal Society!

After his BA in Kolkata, Bose went to England to study medicine. But when problems of health prevented him from completing this course, he shifted to physical sciences and took his BA and B.Sc. from Cambridge and London universities in 1884. His career as a student is not very well documented, but one of his professors in Cambridge was the celebrated Lord Rayleigh, who had done fundamental theoretical work on the scattering of electromagnetic radiation, like visible light. Bose's subsequent work suggests that he had imbibed the atmosphere of experiment and discovery that was sweeping the scientific world at the time.

Bose returned to India in 1885 and began work as a professor of physics at Presidency College, Kolkata. It is a measure of the precision of his thinking that when the college offered him a salary less than that paid to his European colleagues, Bose refused the salary entirely and worked gratis for all of three years. His protest was successful and he was finally paid the full salary, with arrears.

At Presidency College, Bose proved to be a gifted and popular teacher, with classes replete with experiments and practical demonstrations. He found physics itself exciting and to convey the magic to his students he animated his lectures with examples and anecdotes and stratagems aimed at bringing out the unity of basic principles behind natural things. Many of his students went on to make important contributions to the sciences. Among them was S.N. Bose, the statistical physicist, after whom a family of elementary, subatomic particles, the Bosons, is named!

What Bose found lacking in Indian colleges and universities at the time was facilities for research. His efforts to develop such facilities in Presidency College were stonewalled for many years. But, indomitable of spirit, Bose set up a laboratory with rudimentary equipment in an abandoned bathroom in the physics department and commenced serious original research!

An area of much interest at the time was the nature of electromagnetic waves. Electric and magnetic phenomena had been studied for a century and it was known that moving electric charges, or currents, had magnetic effects. This is the feature that is used to drive an electric motor, with the help of a current. The opposite, that varying magnetic fields could give rise to currents in conductors, as happens in a dynamo, was also well known. These attributes had been refined to an exact mathematical theory, which went on to say that an electric charge that moved to and fro sent out a wave of combined electric and magnetic effects, or an electromagnetic wave. An example of such waves was ordinary visible light, which showed wave-like properties.

Taking off from the theory, Heinrich Hertz had demonstrated through experiments in the laboratory that varying electric currents did give rise to a combination of electric and magnetic effects, which moved out as waves. These waves behaved in all ways like ordinary light, but with a much larger wavelength. The dimensions of the waves of visible light are a thousandth of a millimetre, while the man-made Hertz waves had dimensions from centimetres to metres. Hertz waves then got scattered much less than shorter waves and could move 'around' small obstacles, much like the waves of the sea which are not affected by a post sticking out of the water! This was an exciting phenomenon and there was much interest in applying this effect to convey signals over a distance.

It was in this area of the properties of Hertzian waves that Bose worked in that makeshift laboratory. He set up electrical equipment to generate alternating currents and 'sparks' of electricity, which would give off electromagnetic waves. While Hertz had used generators about a metre high, Bose used much smaller equipment, less than a centimetre across, to work with smaller, 'centimetre' waves.

Along with these generators of waves, Bose developed ways

to detect the waves at a distance, when the waves would be much weaker. One kind of detector was loops or coiled wires, like antennas. This was suitable for detecting electromagnetic waves with long wavelength. But for the smaller waves with which Bose was working, he developed cavities and resonators, with the appropriate dimensions. And finally, to detect the waves which were rapidly alternating, he developed a device known as junction detectors. These were sharp iron points pressing upon an iron contact, and they worked as detectors because these junctions could act like one-way gates for electric current.

A wave of electromagnetic radiation consists of electric and magnetic effects that are rapidly rising to a maximum in one direction, falling to zero and then rising to a maximum in the other direction. When such a wave resonates in a cavity, it sets up weak currents which alternate in direction in the same way. But when the wave impinges on the junction detector, which is connected to a power supply, it allows current to pass during one half of the alternating cycle, and not during the other, opposite half. The result is that a current, which is many times stronger than the wave received, flows through the junction in one direction only, and the current can then be measured by an instrument!

During those years, J.C. Bose also developed detectors using galena crystals. These crystals are like the junctions just described, except that the components involved are at the *atomic* level, in the structure of the crystal. The use of these crystals, in fact, was like the transistor technology that was developed many years later. In the words of Sir Neville Mott, Nobel laureate in 1977 for his own contributions to solid-state electronics, 'J.C. Bose was at least sixty years ahead of his time.'

Using this equipment, J.C. Bose conducted research on the properties of electromagnetic waves in the half centimetre region and the effectiveness of metallic tubes to conduct such waves, functioning as 'wave guides'. This work was a very important contribution of J.C. Bose to the world of communications.

In the course of his researches, Bose developed an effective scheme for transmission and reception of millimetre electromagnetic waves. In 1895, Bose demonstrated to an excited audience of the Asiatic Society, Kolkata, the wireless transmission of radio waves over a distance of 75 feet, through masonry, to ring a bell and to ignite gunpowder! In 1896, after another such demonstration, the *Daily Chronicle* of England reported, 'The inventor (J.C. Bose) has transmitted signals to a distance of nearly a mile and herein lies the first and obvious and exceedingly valuable application of this new theoretical marvel.'

These distances were nearly the limit to which millimetre waves could be used. Transmission over longer distances required waves of longer wavelength, a development initiated by A.S. Popov in Russia and given a practical shape by Marconi in 1898. Although the commercial and practical success belonged to Marconi, the engineer, it was J.C. Bose who had developed and demonstrated this technology from the standpoint of a scientist. In fact, a vital component of the arrangement was the device that receives the wireless signal, known as the coherer. It is now recognized that the design of the coherer used by Marconi for the celebrated demonstration of 1897, was none but what was devised by Bose.

It is not that Bose had not recognized the commercial value of his discovery. He had immediately sent details of his work to Lord Rayleigh and Lord Kelvin in England, and they had recognized the worth of their former student and colleague's breakthrough. Bose also went on lecture tours in Europe and USA in 1896–97 and 1901–02. But at no time did he make any secret of the design of the coherer, which he felt anyone was free to use and exploit. In a letter to Rabindranath Tagore, he said,

> . . . the proprietor of a reputed telegraph company . . . came himself with a Patent form in hand . . . He proposed to take half of the profit and finance the business in the bargain. This multimillionaire came to me abegging. My friend, I wish you could see that terrible attachment for gain in this country, that all-engaging lucre, that lust for money and more money. Once caught in that trap there would have been no way out for me.

Apart from the spectacular transmission and detection of radio signals, J.C. Bose's work in the last decade of the nineteenth century greatly advanced the understanding of short electromagnetic waves and the use of metallic cavities and tubes for their transmission, and horns and curved surfaces to guide them. Decades later, when the limitations of conventional wireless technology were understood, these principles became relevant in the development of microwave communication, radar, digital signals over cables and optical fibre technology.

While the commercial value of what he had discovered was getting taken over by trade and industry, Bose trained his attention on the academic issue of the millimetre waves itself. During the presentation of his experiments before the Royal Institution in 1897, he had already started proposing that millimetre waves should be getting generated by the sun, and speculating on the reasons for our not receiving any of them! Perhaps there were components in either the solar or the earth's atmosphere that were responsible, he suggested. The concepts, again, were precocious and prophetic, for microwave radiation from the sun was discovered in 1942, and in 1944 it was found that water vapour strongly absorbed radiation in the 1.2 mm range.

His discoveries in radio waves apart, a lingering interest of Bose ever since his undergraduate days, was botany. During the early 1900s he used the expertise that he had developed in making precise and minute measurements and his knowledge of electromagnetic waves to investigate the effect of these waves on growth of plants.

Using the same sophisticated methods of investigating the inanimate and invisible properties of light and radio waves, Bose studied the reaction of plant forms to radiation, temperature, trauma (injury), sounds and all physical conditions, generally. Researchers in biology are usually hampered by not being specialists in the instruments they use, even microscopes. The result is that the content of research is limited by the training of the researcher and these aspects of plant behaviour are not examined, by default. But Bose was an expert in instrumentation in addition to being a trained botanist.

The outcome was a formidable catalogue of data and also the birth of the field of plant biophysics. The work was widely acclaimed and greatly influenced the course of research in the life sciences. At that time, the world of medicine and psychiatry was seriously examining the physiological or purely chemical-electric origin of emotions. Bose's work raised the opposite question, that if plants underwent similar chemical-electrical changes when exposed to stimuli, could it not be held that they experienced emotions too?

The assertion may today appear to be facetious and not strictly scientific. But the question raised is in fact totally scientific, in not discarding an idea without objective examination of the facts. Whether or not we agree about the 'irritability' of plants, a subject studied by Bose, there is no denying the value of Bose's painstaking measurement of changes in electrical and chemical activity in the cells of plants under all kinds of environmental pollution!

All through the early part of the twentieth century, J.C. Bose travelled widely and lectured about his findings and conjectures in varied forums. And everywhere he was received as a remarkable man of science from India. He was knighted by the British Crown in 1917 and elected fellow of the Royal Society in 1920. He retired from Presidency College in 1915, but was appointed professor emeritus and the government awarded him a pension of Rs 1,500 a month, a formidable sum for the times!

Apart from his versatile scientific ability, J.C. Bose was also an aesthete and a man of the arts. He was a good friend of Rabindranath Tagore and was president of the Bengali Sahitya Parishad, or the Bengali Literature Society. He had literary friends further afield and was on intimate terms with the English playwright George Bernard Shaw, the French writer Romain Rolland, Sister Nivedita, and many prominent personalities of the early twentieth century. The walls of the Bose Institute, which he founded, were decorated with valuable frescos and displayed the old masters.

After he retired from Presidency College, Bose dedicated

himself to building, for India, what he had always considered crucial for scientific progress—a well-endowed facility for research in the sciences. In 1917, J.C. Bose founded the Bose Institute in Kolkata with the purpose of investigating fully, as he recorded, 'the many and ever-opening problems of the nascent science which includes both life and non-life'. Bose was the director of this institute up to 1937, when he died.

The Institute is now one of the leading establishments in India and is marked by the variety of fields where research work is done. It has departments in physics, chemistry, botany, microbiology, biochemistry and biophysics, molecular cellular genetics, animal physiology, environmental sciences, and immunotechnology. In 1988, a bioinformatics centre was added, with work on genetic engineering, biocrystallography, biocomputing and molecular modelling. The diversity of the areas of the Institute's interests reflects the versatility of its founder!

SRINIVASA RAMANUJAN

SRINIVASA RAMANUJAN WAS PERHAPS THE FIRST of the true 'moderns' of Indian science. He quietly took for India a place of honour in the stream of discovery in the sciences that swept through the Western world since the seventeenth century. In mathematics, India's achievements included the development of the decimal system and the discovery of zero, and the list of Indian mathematicians included greats like Bhaskara and Brahmagupta. In the Indian tradition there were also clever results and quick ways to work out problems in arithmetic. But abstract and analytical work that was systematic and gave importance to proving things, progressing from particular results to general principles, was first discovered by the Greeks and then continued in Western mathematics. It is true that India had attained, since ancient times, proficiency in architecture and metallurgy, but in the nineteenth century Europe was the leader in a multitude of fields, including those of engineering, ship-building, chemical technology, spinning and weaving . . . and also the sciences!

The education system introduced in India by the British was based upon the system in England and basic, formal mathematics was also taught. The sharpest of Indians excelled in law, commerce, engineering and mathematics, even establishing a mathematical society. This society tried to make available to its members expensive books and journals from America and England. But still, the purpose of the educational system was only to supply the British regime with literate and competent workers. It was not to create philosophers and thinkers, which was the objective of the universities in England.

It was in this unlikely setting that Srinivasa Aaiyangar Ramanujan astonished the Western world by what he achieved. He looked deep into the simple, practical mathematics that was taught to him by the existing system and went on to rediscover much of what the greatest of European mathematicians had done in the last three centuries. And he went further, to add to mathematics whole new areas of research and marvels that are studied and analysed to this day.

Ramanujan was born on 22 December 1887 in Erode, on the banks of the Cauvery, 245 miles south-west of Chennai. His father was an accountant in a firm that dealt in saris and textiles in Kumbakonam, and does not appear to have had any noticeable influence on Ramanujan. Ramanujan's mother was a much stronger personality. She took most of the decisions in the household and was of some refinement. She was a singer of bhajans in the local temple, which also helped her to earn a few rupees to supplement the family income.

And so, in the placid temple town of Kumbakonam, Ramanujan spent his childhood, reared as a traditional Hindu boy, his head full of scriptures, religion, the temple and rituals unchanged for centuries.

Till Ramanujan was ten years old, he attended Kangayan Primary School. In 1897, he stood first in the district in English, Tamil, arithmetic and geography in the primary school examination. And the following year he enrolled in the English-language high school, Town High.

Town High was an institution of some tradition, with revered teachers and a record of fine students. Ramanujan made a mark early, and in just a year after he had enrolled, became a legend in mathematics. Very soon his companions turned to him for help, and he began to challenge his teachers. Just about this time, Ramanujan came across the book *Trigonometry*, by S.L. Loney, the classic English high school textbook on the subject, which also contained some advanced material. By the time Ramanujan was thirteen he had mastered his Loney, an achievement that would do an undergraduate proud!

Ramanujan soon learnt many difficult things, like cubic equations, a topic that any but professional mathematicians would keep at a safe distance. He was at home with the mysteries of pi (π) and e. Pi, or the ratio of the circumference of a circle to its diameter, and usually shown as $^{22}/_7$, is a number that is remarkable in that it can never, even in theory, be exactly evaluated. Another such number is e, connected with how fast a thing, for example a bank deposit, grows if the compound interest is added not once a year, or even once a month, but continuously, at intervals as close to zero as they can get. Pi and e are also related, in a surprising way, involving the use of imaginary numbers, or quantities that involve the square root of -1! Subjects like these were Ramanujan's close companions. And students two or three years senior came to him with problems that had plagued them for weeks, which he would proceed to solve at a glance!

Trigonometry itself, as the name suggests, is a study of triangles, and associates the ratios of the sides of triangles with the angle between the sides. A more sophisticated way to look at these ratios is to trace a link between angles, triangles and circles and to work in terms of infinitely long series of numbers. While still at school, Ramanujan developed, on his own, this approach to trigonometric ratios. He was rather mortified when he learnt some time later that the method had been discovered by Euler in the eighteenth century!

By the time Ramanujan finished school he had become a celebrity for his talent in mathematics, winning prizes and accolades. He joined Government College, also in Kumbakonam, as an FA or 'First Arts' student in 1904, with a scholarship.

So far, despite all the notoriety that comes of academic brilliance, Ramanujan had been a conventionally well-behaved lad and quite in his mother's control. He was phenomenal in mathematics, it was true, but he did reasonably well in other subjects too. However, once in university, mathematics seemed to take hold of Ramanujan's very being and brought to the surface a wilfulness, an almost irrational, eccentric aspect that resulted in his having to drop out of regular formal, university education, for many years.

The stage for this transformation was probably set by the influence of a mathematical work that Ramanujan had come upon just before he left school. The book in question was Carr's *Synopsis of Elementary Results in Pure Mathematics*, a collection of important mathematical results, with just the results stated without proof or explanation. Although not a work of any importance by itself, the book had the effect of introducing the young and brilliant Ramanujan to the wonders of mathematics as developed by greats like Newton, Euler and Laplace since the seventeenth century.

George Shoobridge Carr, the author, in fact, was a mathematician of average ability who had compiled his synopsis mainly as a volume of reference for students. During the eighteenth and early nineteenth century, students of mathematics in England were preoccupied, almost insanely obsessed, with the challenge of the Tripos, the infamously testing examination of the University of Cambridge.

The Tripos called for incredible facility with the most demanding topics in mathematics and consisted of a set of problems, solving even one of which would do a student credit. Success in the Tripos demanded that students solved many of them and a good rank in the Tripos usually assured for a student a bright career in any line of work he chose.

Tutoring students for the Tripos had hence become a paying occupation. Carr, who had an MA in mathematics from Cambridge University, was an enthusiastic teacher. After years of painstaking work in helping students master the vast areas that the Tripos required them to, Carr compiled his *Synopsis*. A listing of important results, it was seemingly just a vast catalogue of theorems and formulae, perhaps not of much utility except in conjunction with all the material that went before.

But to the curious and mathematically almost intuitive Ramanujan, Carr's *Synopsis* proved a wonderland of challenges that took him swiftly through what may have been the course of many years of conventional training. To be fair to the *Synopsis*, although it states results with just, occasionally, a hint of a proof, it does have a 'progression' of results leading from one to another. It is no guide through the history of mathematics but is at least a list of the highlights in nearly the correct order!

The lack of detailed proofs forced Ramanujan to work them out himself, thereby developing insight and discovering new results and extensions along the way. One of the definite results of this apprenticeship to Carr was that Ramanujan did not learn the rigorous method of Western mathematics which involved clearly stating the assumptions and then systematically arriving at conclusions, with proofs. Instead, following the example of *Synopsis*, much of Ramanujan's original work consists of brilliant results simply stated, with generations of researchers and students who came after him having to plod to find the proof.

The main result of this exposure to Carr was that by the time Ramanujan was in college, he worked on mathematics and little else. When he finished his FA, his performance in mathematics, surely enough, was brilliant, but he failed in English and did dismally in other subjects. His scholarship was withdrawn and he had to drop out of Government College, Kumbakonam.

The months that followed were tense and troubled, with Ramanujan a drain on his family and far from prepared, academically or temperamentally, for any kind of paying work, though he tried to make ends meet by giving tuitions. It all led to Ramanujan running away from home, first at the age of seventeen, when he went as far as Vishakhapatnam, on the eastern coast of Andhra Pradesh. What he did at Vishakhapatnam, and how he supported himself, is not very clear, except that in a few months he was traced by his family and coaxed back home. He obviously found the pressure of being expected to come to some good too hard to bear, because he ran away from home more than once, till, at the age of nineteen, he found a place in Pachaiyappa's College, Chennai, to have another go at the First Arts course.

Pachaiyappa's was an institution with a fine academic tradition and boasted an enlightened faculty in mathematics. As before, Ramanujan thrived in mathematics but neglected all else. Ramanujan's biographer, Robert Kanigel, narrates in *The Man Who Knew Infinity*, that answering a question on the digestive system of the rabbit, which was taught as part of the course on physiology, Ramanujan reportedly wrote in his examination paper, 'Sir this is my undigested product of the chapter on the digestive system.'

Needless to say, in December 1906, Ramanujan failed the FA examination. He failed again in 1907. The only work he could do was to tutor students in mathematics and this he did more to indulge himself than to help students clear the examinations. This source of livelihood too soon disappeared and Ramanujan was left with nothing to do but live on the bounty of friends and relatives, and to fill his notebooks with mathematics.

Ramanujan worked incessantly and crammed his now celebrated notebooks with theorems and discoveries. The notebooks have survived and are a record of the vast canvas of pure mathematics that Ramanujan worked with in those years. He had initially set out to put down proofs for the results in Carr's *Synopsis*, but soon went much further. Each theorem brought out new and unimagined refinements and discoveries. The notebooks are a meandering record of a fevered creativity, in notations that are difficult for any but a talented mathematician to comprehend. The later notebooks were edited versions, where the material has been composed and annotated for publication. Yet, there are still intuitive leaps and steps encapsulating whole flights in one, whose unravelling has formed for many a student the work of a lifetime!

During the years 1908 to 1912, Ramanujan worked as well as his straitened circumstances would allow. He moved from Kumbakonam to Chennai, to Villipuram, near Pondicherry, or wherever a sponsor or kindly soul would keep him, and he constantly worked at his mathematics. The notebooks were edited and put in order, as a kind of visiting card to seek whatever employment he could get, to enable him to afford two meals a day. He was also able to get his first path-breaking papers published in the *Journal of the Indian Mathematical Society*.

These first papers dealt, like much of his work, with series of numbers extending to infinity. An instance is a number like this:

$$\sqrt{1+2+\sqrt{1+3+\sqrt{1+4+\sqrt{1+5+\sqrt{1+\ldots}}}}}$$

or a square root which contains a square root, which contains a square root, and so on. When this was published in the *Journal* as a problem to challenge readers, no solution was forthcoming for months! Ramanujan's notebooks and papers contained general theorems and stratagems to solve mysteries like these as well as studies of the properties of the maze of mathematical constants and functions, some which were already known and some that Ramanujan discovered.

These publications soon started getting Ramanujan recognition and there began to develop around him a group of friends and admirers. Finally, in 1912, with the help of some of these, Ramanujan got a job as a clerk in the Madras Port Trust. With this backing of a regular income, he was able at last to devote himself seriously to mathematics. He was already twenty-five years old, an age by which mathematicians have generally done their greatest work, and Ramanujan had to hurry to catch up!

It was now that Ramanujan's work came to the notice of Englishmen working in Chennai and they sent portions of his work to abler mathematicians in England for an opinion. The response was hesitant and cautious, but of a quality that convinced Ramanujan that it was in England that he should seek appreciation and educated critique of his work.

So Ramanujan began writing to leading mathematicians in

England, with samples of his work. Initially, the letters seemed to arouse no interest, till, providentially, a brilliant young mathematician at Cambridge, G.H. Hardy, took enthusiastic notice. He was thunderstruck by the incredible originality of the material sent to him by the remarkable Indian clerk.

What followed is historic. Even before Hardy wrote back to Ramanujan, he had set in motion the process of inviting Ramanujan to Cambridge.

Ramanujan baulked at first. Orthodox Hindus believed that crossing the ocean resulted in losing caste. But Hardy's letter also infused him with renewed confidence and a desire for recognition. Hardy and Ramanujan began an exchange of letters on mathematics, and on the strength of this communication Ramanujan got a scholarship of Rs 50 per month from the Madras University in 1913 to work at the university. In 1914, the university offered Ramanujan a scholarship of £250 to work at Cambridge, with a grant of £100 to help with the passage. Ramanujan set out for England.

At Cambridge, Hardy got to work at first hand with the remarkable notebooks containing the theorems, of which some 120 he had seen so far, by post. Soon their character became clearer. A good portion was rediscovery of work that had gone before, even during the forty years that had passed after the publication of Carr's *Synopsis*. Some parts were even incorrect. But a substantial portion, over a third, Hardy could see, was brilliant and mint new! Other commentators have put this portion to almost half.

Hardy undertook in full earnest the task of editing Ramanujan's notebooks for publication. Ramanujan also set to work in the academically electrifying surroundings of

Cambridge. He knew now that a proper university education, like in England, would have trained him in many topics in mathematics that had been discovered by talented men before him. This would not only have saved him the trouble of discovering them again, to no credit, but would have launched him onto greater things. In 1915, a year after his arrival in England, Ramanujan published a flurry of papers, much of them being new work.

These papers and the work of subsequent years covered novel approaches to evaluating the random and infinite digits in the expansion of the number π, modular forms, divergent series, elliptic integrals, number theory, discoveries in prime numbers, partitions, round numbers . . . These were subjects that gripped contemporary mathematicians, and Ramanujan's unique approach and tremendous intuitive feel for numbers made a deep impact and provoked great interest.

Such was the stature of the work being turned out that Hardy soon felt obliged to propose that Ramanujan be elected as a fellow of Trinity College. Some university politics and perhaps a touch of racism kept this from happening for two years running. This affected Ramanujan in spirit. He was already in poor shape physically, as the English winters had been bitterly cold. He contracted tuberculosis.

Soon after the disappointment pertaining to the Trinity fellowship, he entered Matlock, a TB sanatorium. But the sanatorium could hardly help him, as he was resolutely vegetarian and craved for south Indian food. He was too sick to be mathematically productive and this rankled too.

In the mean time, undeterred by the failure at Trinity, Hardy went on trying to get Ramanujan the recognition he deserved.

In December 1917, Ramanujan was elected to the London Mathematical Society. And just two weeks later, Hardy and eleven other mathematical heavyweights of England nominated Ramanujan for election as a fellow of the Royal Society.

'Distinguished as a pure mathematician, particularly for his investigation of elliptic functions and the theory of numbers' was how he was described in their nomination. In January 1918, the Royal Society published a list of 103 candidates, Ramanujan included, for election.

On the face of it, Ramanujan was facing difficult odds. For a start, he was very young, only thirty-one. Still, Hardy lobbied for him, arguing that 'his claims are such as, in the long run, could not be ignored . . . There is an absolute gulf between him and other mathematical candidates . . .'

In February that year, Ramanujan was elected to the Cambridge Philosophical Society. And then, ten days later, Ramanujan could hardly believe the telegram he received from Hardy. He was elected a fellow of the Royal Society! A few months later, Trinity College also made him a fellow.

The effect on Ramanujan's spirits was such as expected—it resulted in 'a brief period of brilliant invention', in the words of E.H. Neville, professor of mathematics at Cambridge. He had first met Ramanujan at Chennai, in 1914, and had later played a major role in promoting Ramanujan and his work at Cambridge. Ramanujan's health, too, seemed to get a little better. With the end of the war and the sea routes being open once more, it was time now for Ramanujan to return to India, which he did in March 1919.

He arrived in India, as the *Journal of the Indian Mathematical Society* announced, 'in indifferent health'. For a year after this,

Ramanujan did correspond a little with Hardy about theta functions, an area of complex mathematics involving infinities and elliptic ratios, just what was needed to cheer his troubled spirits. But his health deteriorated continuously, till on 26 April 1920 he died, one of the most original mathematicians of the century.

C.V. RAMAN

'I WONDER WHAT MAKES THE SEA BLUE?' C.V. Raman may have thought while on the steamer from England to India. But if he did, it was no idle musing. During the two-week voyage, while his fellow passengers played deck hockey and bingo, Raman conducted experiments with a pocket spectrometer and turned out two scientific papers, one by the time the ship reached Aden and the second as they got into Mumbai. It was the year 1921, and C.V. Raman was returning to India after representing Kolkata University at a congress at London. The question about the blue sea, which the Mediterranean seemed to have provoked, soon led to epochal scientific work and the Nobel Prize!

In 1921, C.V. Raman was the Palit professor of physics at Kolkata University and had gained an international reputation as a formidable man of physics through his research into the theory of sound and musical instruments.

Chandrasekhara Venkata Raman, later Fellow of the Royal Society (FRS) and Nobel laureate, was born in 1888 at Thiruchirapalli, in Tamil Nadu. He finished school at the age of eleven and graduated in physics and English, at the head of his class, at fifteen. Poor health kept him from going to England and he continued at Presidency College, Chennai, from where he received his master's with honours, at the age of eighteen. Ironically, he now entered the civil service, as assistant accountant general, at the age of nineteen with a posting in the auditor general's office, Kolkata.

Happily for science, he found some spare time to keep in touch with physics and managed to do work on the theory of stringed instruments and Indian drums in the laboratories of the Indian Association for the Cultivation of Science (IACS). This institution, envisioned as an agent for regeneration of modern India, had been set up by Mahendra Lal Sircar, a pioneer in promoting science, in 1876. But it had achieved little of note.

In 1907, Raman saw the IACS sign on his way to work by tram one day, and jumped at the possibility of continuing to work with physics. He moved to a house near the IACS premises and would come in early in the morning and stay till he had to leave for work. He would then come after office hours and stay till late in the evening. Thanks to Raman's work, the IACS attracted an impressive list of men of science and over the years more than satisfied its founder's dream.

From 1907 to 1917, Raman worked at the IACS on a variety of topics, focussing primarily the science of sound, vibration of strings and drums, and optics and the behaviour of light. He published his work in the world's leading journals and began to be widely known.

In 1916, Sir Ashutosh Mukherjee, a brilliant man of letters and a long-time observer of Raman's work, was appointed vice chancellor of Kolkata University. Within a year he managed to create a special chair for the promotion of physics, the Palit professorship, and offered the post to Raman. Raman gladly gave up his promising career in the civil service and accepted the opportunity for full-time devotion to his first love, the pursuit of science.

But getting back to the question about the colour of the sea. The reason behind the blue colour of the sky had then been precisely explained by the work of Lord Rayleigh. Visible light was recognized as consisting of waves of electrical and magnetic disturbances, spreading out rather like the ripples on the surface of a pond, at the tremendous speed of three hundred thousand kilometres a second. The exact mathematics that applies to waves had perfectly accounted for all of the properties of light, and even its other forms, like radio waves, heat waves and X-rays. These were properties like how it reflects, how it bends in lenses, how radio waves could bounce off the layers of the atmosphere, and so on.

Lord Rayleigh then applied classical physics, to look into how such waves were scattered by specks of dust or even the tiny molecules of the air.

To understand scattering, we could look at the ripples on the surface of a pond. Consider what happens if there were a twig and a thick post sticking out of the water. The twig hardly seems to affect the passage of the ripples. But in the case of the post, the course of the original wave is broken and another set of ripples spreads out from the post itself. These secondary ripples, which spread out from the post, are the scattered waves.

It seems evident that the post has this effect, but not the twig, mainly because the dimensions of the post are comparable to the distance between successive ripples, or their wavelength. The same post, if sticking out of the sea, where the waves are many metres apart, would have no effect, rather like the twig in the case of the ripples in the pond.

Rayleigh was able to work out that for the same size of obstructions, the strength of scattering increased very fast as the wavelength got shorter. The strength of scattering of a wave with half the wavelength, in fact, was not just twice as much but sixteen times!

The meaning of this discovery, for the sunlight coming through the atmosphere, was that the light towards the violet side of the spectrum was scattered much more strongly than the light towards the red side of the spectrum. The sunlight that finally hits the surface of the earth is thus a little depleted in components towards the violet side, which explains why the sun looks yellow when we look at it during the day. Late in the evening, when the sunlight is passing through more of the atmosphere because of the slant, the violet end of the spectrum is depleted further and the sun looks orange or red!

This is about the light that comes to us straight from the sun. The light that is scattered in all directions lights up the sky, which in turn, scatters light again towards us. We can imagine that such light, scattered twice over, would largely be towards the violet end, and so it is largely blue!

This was the complete, perfect, elegant explanation for the blue sky. But for the blue sea, the current theory simply said that the sea was blue because it reflected the blue sky! When Raman saw the dazzling blue of the Mediterranean during his voyage, he thought this glib explanation was just not satisfactory. Why could it not be a case of light being scattered by the molecules of water, just like the air, wondered Raman. And so, while the ship sailed, he made careful observations, using the prism, telescope and spectroscope, which he always carried, and came to important conclusions about the scattering of light by molecules, before the end of the voyage.

This work on scattering of light by liquids was, at best, a refinement of work that had already been done on its scattering by air. The other, more important aspect that began bothering Raman at the time was whether the 'quantum' nature of light also played a role in scattering. The wave theory of light, based on the study of electricity and magnetism, was then the pinnacle of success of classical physics and mathematics. But recent discoveries had indicated that the wave theory was not the whole story. Light also displayed a 'particle' or 'corpuscular' behaviour. That light could have a quantum nature did not contradict the wave theory, but was vital in explaining the radiation of heat by warm objects, an area where the wave theory alone had run into a serious problem.

The quantum theory, which overcame this problem, first said that atoms and molecules did not exist in a continuum of energy states, but only in discrete, step-wise, energy levels, separated by 'quanta' of energy. And changes in energy levels corresponded to the emission or absorption of the quantum of energy in the form of photons, or particles of light of the appropriate energy.

Apart from this 'need' for light to have a quantum nature, Einstein's theory of the photoelectric effect, based on light quanta, was a powerful verification. And then, in 1923, Compton had studied an effect where X-rays underwent not just scattering, but a change in wavelength when they bounced off atoms. This effect was so exactly explained if X-rays were considered to exist as quanta that gained or lost energy during impact with an electron, just like billiard balls do when they bounce off each other, that there remained little doubt about the validity of the quantum theory. Kramers and Heisenberg, in fact, had also suggested that the same thing was possible in the ordinary scattering of light!

Yet, in spite of these advancements, the classic Rayleigh theory was so *de rigueur* and exact, that scientists, Niels Bohr and Max Planck included, were loath to think there could be anything more to say on the subject. It is a mark of Raman's objectivity and scientific honesty that he felt he must still look for evidence of quantum effects in the scattering of visible light by liquids.

The next few years at the IACS laboratory were devoted entirely to the study of the scattering of lights by liquids. The Association now had some brilliant students and a good bit of data was generated. The experimental set-up required a source of intense, white light. This was provided by reflecting the sun's rays into the lab with the help of a mirror. This light was passed through a violet filter and then allowed to pass through the liquid being studied. The light scattered at right angles was examined by viewing the liquid from the side, using a telescope.

Naturally, some violet light was seen, and even if a violet filter was used, the violet light came through. The objective of the experiments was to introduce a green filter, or a yellow filter and see whether scattered light of colours *other* than violet could be seen.

The scattered violet light itself was extremely feeble and there was no doubt that if there was any light of other colours to be detected, it would also be feeble indeed. The incident beam, derived from bright sunlight, was already the most intense that could be mustered at those times. To help the observer detect the feeblest of scattered components, he was placed in a darkened chamber, four feet square, for an hour before the experiment was started. This was to prime the observer's eyes to maximum sensitivity, a method that Lord Rutherford and his students had used in their celebrated discovery of the atomic nucleus. Raman's box in the IACS laboratory was facetiously called the 'black hole of Kolkata'.

One by one, the researchers began to report that there was a 'modified' scattered light, that is, light of a different colour. Classical Rayleigh theory was emphatic in saying that the scattered light would be of the same colour. How could the observations be reconciled? A ready explanation was that this was not scattered light but a case of fluorescence.

Fluorescence is the property whereby atoms in a substance absorb the incident light, and then, usually after a short delay (a very short delay, in microseconds), shift to an intermediate state and emit light of a different wavelength. This is what happens in the common, domestic tube light. The tube is filled with a gas at low pressure, which allows a discharge of electricity, emitting light of a particular colour, often in the ultraviolet. This light falls on the fluorescent coating of the tube, which then emits the 'near white' light of fluorescent lamps.

Raman and his experimenters could not be sure that the modified component they were seeing was really a new wavelength in the scattered light or a case of fluorescence. As fluorescence is often due to impurities, they repeated the experiments with greater and greater purity. But still they saw the modified component. By 1925, the team had noticed the effect in fifty liquids.

Raman now began to seriously suspect that they were dealing with a kind of Compton effect in the visible portion of the spectrum. The research work was stepped up and more and more data was accumulated. An important new piece of data was that the modified scattering was polarized light.

The scattering of light and its transverse waves can be

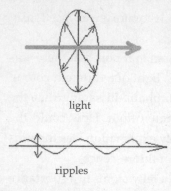

light

ripples

understood by comparing it to ripples on a pond. In the case of the ripples, the water at any point is moving up and down, while the ripples move along the surface. In the case of a light wave too, the changes in the electric field are at right angles to, or transverse to, the direction of the light beam.

But unlike in the case of ripples, in the case of light, there are no fixed 'up' or 'down' directions and the electric wave can be in any direction, so long as it is at right angles to the direction of the beam. In a usual beam of light, we have all possible orientations of the electric wave.

When light is generated not by randomly oriented atoms, but in a given direction only by atoms oriented just so, the electric waves in the light beam are all along one axis, and light like this is said to be polarized.

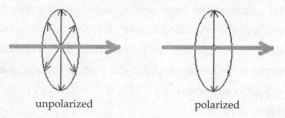

unpolarized   polarized

In Rayleigh's theory of scattering, which was a theory that worked, scattering was explained as happening due to atoms in particular orientations. And so, scattered light was found to be polarized. But in the case of fluorescence, absorption of energy and its emission were separate events, and the orientation of the atoms that participate was not important. Fluorescent light was hence found to be unpolarized.

What Raman's team had seen was that the modified ray in the scattering experiments was polarized. This was a strong reason for it being *not* a case of fluorescence, but really an odd instance of scattering with a change in the wavelength!

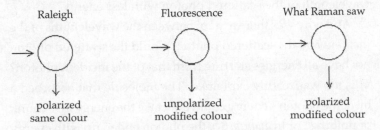

Raleigh	Fluorescence	What Raman saw
polarized same colour	unpolarized modified colour	polarized modified colour

The definitive experiment, on 28 February 1928, was with the incident light passed not just through the blue filter, but also through a uranium glass, which made the incident beam not just in the *range* of violet, but a very narrow band of the spectrum.

And when the scattered beam was viewed it was not through a green or other filter, but through a spectroscope, which splits the light coming in into its components, like a prism. What was seen, was one line, which was the original light, and next to it, another faint line, the new colour generated in the scattering!

This was a definite, startling result, that in scattering of visible light by liquids, in addition to Rayleigh's scattering, there arose a scattered component with a change in wavelength, just like in the scattering of X-rays by electrons!

The very next day Raman called a press conference and in weeks the news was the sensation in scientific circles the world over. The explanation, which Raman also published, was easily seen as the incident photon having transferred some of its energy to the molecule off which it was scattered, thus leaving the scattered photon with less energy. Using the relation that Planck and Einstein had developed, to connect the wavelength of a photon with its energy, it was easy to work out the longer wavelength of the scattered photon with less energy.

And why was there a 'gap' between the wavelengths of the incident and the scattered photon? Could the scattered photon not have all energies starting from that of the incident photon? This too was readily explained. The molecule that absorbed a bit of the photon's energy could only take the energy in a 'chunk or nothing', or in *quanta*. So, the photon ended up with energy reduced (or increased) in steps, and not continuously.

The discovery was indeed a momentous one. On the one hand, it was emphatic proof of the quantum theory. It was a courageous, needle-in-a-haystack search for a misty possibility that was suggested by a still tentative theory, a search that resulted in fixing firm signposts on the way to new discoveries. On the side of applications, the 'Raman spectra' of materials soon became a sensitive tool to study the low energy, vibration and rotation modes of molecules, an area that thrives nearly unchanged to this day.

Recognition was not far in coming, either. Rutherford announced the discovery in the Royal Society, the British government conferred a knighthood and in 1930, Raman became India's first Nobel laureate for science! The 1920s were memorable years in the development of physics as a discipline. For an Indian scientist, working entirely in India, to have a place of honour during those times was electrifying.

Apart from being an active researcher and having published

profusely for two decades, Raman had also been the builder of a school of well-trained scientists at the IACS. In 1933, he took over as the first Indian director of the Tata Institute of Sciences, the forerunner of the Indian Institute of Science, Bangalore. During the next fifteen years that Raman spent at the Institute, he did much to set up and develop the physics department into one of international repute, apart from training and inspiring a generation of world-class scientists. During these years, he also founded the Indian Academy of Sciences whose journal *Proceedings of the Indian Academy of Sciences* was the first of the many reputed journals published in the country. He retired from the Institute in 1948 and set up the Raman Institute a few kilometres away. A notable feature of this institute was that it had been funded entirely by private donations.

Raman continued work in the research and exposition of science till 1970. On 2 October 1970, he delivered the customary Mahatma Gandhi Memorial lecture at the Raman Institute. Soon after, he fell ill, and on 21 November he passed away.

S.N. Bose

Respected Sir,

I have ventured to send you the accompanying article for your perusal and opinion. You will see that I have tried to deduce the coefficient . . . in Planck's law independent of classical electrodynamics.

In 1924, Satyendra Nath Bose, thirty years of age and a reader in physics at the Dhaka University, hesitantly sent the celebrated Albert Einstein a four-page paper on a new way to arrive at Max Planck's formula for the spectrum of radiation from a warm object. The result was the discovery of a principle fundamental to natural processes, which was to play a pivotal role in the subsequent development of physics.

The questions of the distribution of radiation from a warm object had been puzzling scientists for a good quarter of a century. It was known by then that light and radiated heat were forms of electromagnetic waves. While visible light was in wavelengths that the eyes could detect, waves of heat radiation were longer, longer even the waves of red light, in the infrared region.

Scientists had been able to analyse these heat waves, like they do with white light, using a prism. They found that a warm object radiated heat at not just one wavelength, but over a range of wavelengths, with peak radiation at one wavelength. They found that this peak moves to shorter wavelengths, that is, closer to visible light, as the body gets warmer. We can easily imagine that this is true, because we know that very hot objects become 'red hot' and start radiating in the visible region. And as the objects get even hotter, they get closer to white hot!

Now the issue was to find a good theoretical way of being

able to calculate how much energy would be radiated at what wavelength by a body at a particular temperature.

This was also not the only problem in physics which puzzled scientists at the time. Till the end of the nineteenth century, it had looked like we were on the verge of understanding almost everything about nature. Newton had formulated the laws of motion and the movement of the heavenly bodies was understood. The rules followed by gases, when heated or compressed, had been worked out. The steam engine and the petrol engine had been invented. Electricity and magnetism were understood and the electric bulb, telephone and wireless had become realities. It seemed as if the physical world had been fully comprehended.

But soon developments disturbed this satisfied world view. Madame Curie's discovery of radioactivity, a new kind of radiation that emerged from some metals, defied explanation. Then came the virtual overturning of the apple cart by Einstein. Einstein redefined our very concepts of time and measurement. Thompson and Rutherford showed that the atom itself consisted of tiny particles with a negative charge around a massive, positively charged core. The existing theory could not explain how such a thing could exist. Would the two parts not attract and neutralize each other? If the electrons were going around the nucleus, like a solar system in miniature, would the charged particles not radiate energy and slow down?

The breakthrough came in the form of an answer to the old problem of the radiation spectrum of warm objects. To understand the way objects radiated heat, scientists had assumed that they contained millions and millions of tiny, elemental oscillators, which vibrated and radiated energy.

When the objects got hotter, the vibrations were more energetic, as was the radiation. The 'colour', or the wavelength at which most of the radiation was given off, also moved up spectrum when the object grew hotter. While the body was radiating energy in this way, it also absorbed some energy from the radiation of surrounding objects. If the surroundings were cooler, the object would lose more heat than it gained, and cool down. Otherwise, it would gain more than it radiated and warm up. In time, the temperature would stabilize when the amount of heat lost was equivalent to the amount absorbed.

Studies of systems with huge numbers of components, which resulted in a steady 'average' behaviour of the whole, was the basis of the theories of gases. Very accurate and clever techniques had been developed for the study of these theories during the preceding century.

The scientists of the time first treated an object as if its elemental oscillators were vibrating with all possible energies. From this, given the total energy, they worked out at what energy most of the oscillators would be bunched, what fraction of the oscillators could be at a slightly lower, and a slightly higher frequency, and so on. This exercise helped them work out the frequency at which the object would radiate the most, and how much it would radiate at higher and lower frequencies. It was somewhat like deciding how much different groups of people would earn and spend, given the total income of a country.

The first law to be formulated was Wien's law and it seemed to agree with the experiment, up to a limit. It gave the correct distribution of energy radiated for a range of frequencies, but went off the mark outside the range. A better law was Rayleigh's law and then the Rayleigh-Jeans's law. These laws all worked for a portion of the radiation spectrum and not across the whole width.

This was when the celebrated Max Planck divined that if he took it that the oscillators could not be vibrating at *all* energy levels, but only at levels very close together, separated only by 'steps', called 'quanta', the equations fell into place. With this, Planck had cracked the black body radiation problem and also hit upon the 'quantum theory'.

The breakaway notion, that nature grew not continuously but in steps, set the world of physics afire. Niels Bohr snapped up the idea and proposed his model of the atom, and Einstien proposed that electromagnetic radiation was not pure wave but packets of energy. These packets, later named photons, were soon detected in experiments, and physic textbook was being rewritten.

It was at this point in time that Professor Satyendra Nath Bose penned that inspired letter to the celebrated Albert Einstein.

Satyendra Nath Bose was born in 1894 in Kolkata, the oldest of the seven children of Surendranath Bose, an engineer in the East India Railway. Young Satyendra Nath was a keen and able scholar and impressed his teachers with his intelligence and industry. He went on to Presidency College, Kolkata, where he had the gifted Jagadish Chandra Bose as a teacher and vibrant fellow students, including Meghnad Saha. After he took his master's degree in 1915, he and some others, motivated by public spiritedness as well as by nationalism, pressed for the opening of a centre for advanced physics and mathematics in Kolkata University. In 1916, this effort succeeded and S.N. Bose worked there as lecturer in physics for the next five years.

In 1921 he was appointed reader in physics at Dhaka University, which was part of the province of Bengal at the time. At Dhaka, Bose continued the drive commenced at Kolkata to improve facilities for the study of physics. One key area was the availability of the best books and the latest research papers. As many of these were not in English, but in French or German, Bose arranged for English translations to be made. It was in the course of this effort that Bose came to translate Einstein's papers on the General Theory of Relativity. The translation rights, had, in fact, been given to Methuen of England, who protested. But Einstein himself agreed and the translation was allowed to appear.

Bose kept abreast with the latest developments in physics the world over, particularly in the exciting area of black body radiation where much intense study was happening. Planck had studied hot objects as a collection of 'oscillators' and had come to an exact expression for the radiation spectrum, by proposing that the energy levels of the oscillators were 'quantized'. Einstein was not quite satisfied with the way this was done and introduced a refinement by saying that the radiation itself consisted of 'quanta' of energy, the photons. He looked at the problem not as one about oscillators, but as that of a cavity filled with photons that kept getting absorbed and emitted by the walls of the cavity. With this model for the radiating body, and with the help of Wien's law, Einstein was able to arrive at Planck's expression for the distribution of the energy radiated.

Einstein had made use of statistical methods similar to the ones used to derive the gas laws, treating the photons in the cavity in the same manner as the molecules of gas in a container.

The kinetic theory of gases, or the statistical distribution of energies of a number of particles in a container, had been developed to some sophistication.

In the case of a gas, the millions of molecules of the gas share the total energy. This could happen in a number of ways. For instance, a few molecules could be moving very, very fast, while the rest, which had to make do with the remaining energy, would be lethargic. Or else, some molecules may be very sluggish, driving the others to move rather fast. The way to work out the most likely distribution of energies was to see which distribution was possible in the most different ways, given the myriad particles involved, so as to retain the same total energy.

When a few molecules shared most of the energy, the distribution was possible in the number of ways the few molecules could be selected from the total number of molecules. If more molecules were to share the energy, this would be possible in the number of ways the larger group could be selected. It is like picking a red ball out of a bag that contains two green balls and ten red balls. There are more ways in which *some* red ball could be picked and so, picking a red ball is more likely.

This line of thinking takes us to the answer. In the case of molecules, if there were ten molecules in all and just two were to use a greater portion of the energy, in how many ways could groups of two be formed from the ten? It can be worked out that there are forty-five ways to form pairs from a group of ten. In the case where three molecules shared the energy, in place of just two, we find that there are 120 ways to form groups of three, from a population of ten. And to form groups of four, there are 210 ways, and 252 ways to form group of five!

In the case of the billions of particles in even a small sample of gas, the ways to have the most 'average' distribution of energies is so overwhelmingly in the majority that we have the completely 'uniform' behaviour of gases that we are familiar with! This is why, given a volume of gas at a certain energy, the gas behaves the same way all over, and never ends up with all the fast atoms bunching up on side, to make the container appear hotter.

So Einstein had used methods similar to these to deal with his 'gas' of photons and had managed, with a bit of help from Wien's law, to arrive at Planck's relation. An implicit assumption in the method used with gases is that each molecule, in principle, could be identified, so that the different combinations of particle speeds, but with the same energy, could be considered separate and counted.

Bose had been following this research and he felt that even what Einstein had done was a bit contrived, as it depended on Wien's law. The law was an external input, not a natural consequence of the photons being considered to behave like a gas. So he devised yet another way of arriving at Planck's formula, but without making assumptions that raised questions about their being valid.

What Bose did was to make the refinement that the photons in his gas, unlike the assumption for molecules in a real gas, were identical or indistinguishable. This immediately makes a big difference in the way distributions work out. Take an example of a red and a blue ball being distributed in three compartments. This is possible in nine ways, like this:

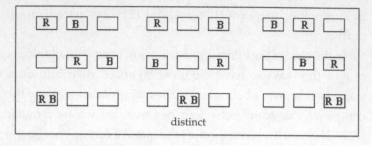

distinct

But if the balls were both the same colour, then the set of the first and third, the second and fifth and the fourth and sixth distributions become the same. Now, only six distributions are possible, like this:

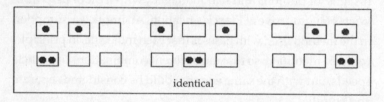

identical

What Bose was doing was to work out a number for all the possible energy states that were possible in the container of the photon gas, something like the compartments in the example, and to see in how many ways the photons, like the balls in the example, could be distributed. Recognizing that the photons were identical was crucial to his line of thought.

Another thing that Bose provided for was that the number of photons, unlike the number of balls, was not fixed. Photons could arise at will, subject only to the condition that the total energy of all the photons was constant. So, along with the detail that each photon could exist in either a 'left-handed' or a 'right-handed' form, Bose worked out the most likely distribution of energies and arrived at the same Planck's law.

An important refinement had been introduced here, that apart from being packets or particles of energy, these photons behaved like identical and indistinguishable entities. This was the work that Bose hesitantly submitted to Einstein on 4 June 1924.

It is not apparent that Bose had anticipated the momentous consequences of his flash of insight in this paper that he had forwarded to Einstein. The *Philosophical Magazine* had already turned it down for publication and Bose now hoped that Einstein would find more value in the paper and agree to get it published in a German journal, at least on the grounds that the author was someone who had translated some of his work into English!

It is to Einstein's credit that he carefully read this paper from an obscure scientist in India and saw at once that what Bose was saying had the greatest significance. He translated the paper into German himself and had it published in *Zeitschrift fur Physik*, with his own comment about its importance. A few weeks later, Einstein wrote a sequel to Bose's paper and followed up with important work that took off from Bose's work itself.

The paper set off a cascade of research worldwide. The idea of the quantum had barely taken root in the world of physics. It was a refinement in scientific thinking, which became significant only at very small dimensions. But this difference at the very small scale is vital for a correct understanding of nature at the larger scale. Much of the advancements in the modern world— transistors, lasers, nuclear power—have followed from this understanding of quantum effects.

One of the features of the atom-scale world is that it is not possible to exactly pinpoint the position of an object. The smaller the object, the greater the uncertainty. When we are dealing with large entities like billiard balls bouncing off one another, we can clearly make out one ball from another. This 'billiard-ball' model of gases, where molecules of a gas were considered distinguishable, was successful with the gas laws, because molecules are still large enough to be distinguished, in principle. But when we enter the world of subatomic particles, or photons, the blurring of the position of the particles prevents us from knowing which particle is which, after a collision. An example is in the picture below.

This uncertainty of position was an aspect of quantum mechanical behaviour that took scientists some years to understand. We can see that once such a thing is understood

Say two balls approach each other, so that they may collide and bounce off.

They may bounce off in either of these two ways:

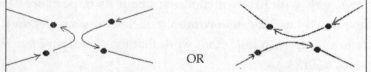

OR

And in principle, we could tell which ball is which after the collison.

But if we were dealing with subatomic particles, the positions are *blurred* at the moment of impact, like this:

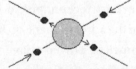

And the identity of the particles, after the impact, is lost!

about very small particles, it follows that the particles need to be treated as indistinguishable. The significance of Bose's discovery is that his insight that particles on the small scale would follow the statistics of indistinguishable particles anticipated the same conclusion that quantum mechanics came to a little later. Bose's discovery that matter sometimes behaved as 'identical particles' helped others in tying up the loose ends about the uncertainty principle and quantum mechanics, and went a long way in developing a theory without contradictions.

The development of Bose's ideas, first by Einstein himself and then by many others, laid the foundation of a whole field called quantum statistics, a cornerstone of later-day physics. Bose, and later Einstein, had worked on one category of the fundamental particles, which were later named Bosons, and the rules for these particles are now known as Bose-Einstein statistics. Some remarkable properties could be predicted for these particles, one of them being that at low energies, they tended to all have the same energy state. Just like the molecules of steam, which condense to form water when cooled, Einstein said that Bosons, when brought to lower energies, would *condense* to this state of trying to all have the same energy level. A consequence of this is the possibility of superfluidity, or the property whereby a substance flows without friction, because adjacent particles tend to *follow*, rather than *oppose* a particle in motion.

This was realized some years later when helium, whose atom is a Boson, could be cooled to low enough a temperature.

S.N. Bose entered the ranks of the unquestioned greats in the world of physics. He was honoured by several universities with doctorates and degrees. He was appointed head of the department of physics at 1926 in Dhaka University. The partition of India was a blow to him, as he considered all Bengal as his home. He was appointed the Khaira professor of physics in Kolkata University in 1945, a post he held till 1956. In 1958 he was elected a Fellow of the Royal Society.

Like many of the very talented, S.N. Bose had varied interests. His scientific work covered areas as far afield as geology and biochemistry. He was a gifted teacher and devoted to his students. Languages came naturally to him and he had deep literary interests. He even worked for and introduced the teaching of physics in Bengali to postgraduate students. He served as a member of the Rajya Sabha and played a role in shaping the country's science policy.

He died in Kolkata, in 1974, at the age of eighty.

MEGHNAD SAHA

THE SUN AND THE STARS HAVE been the stuff of wonder and conjecture since primitive times. Elusive, distant, periodic and regular like nothing else, the heavens naturally evoked images of gods and forces that controlled the lives of those on earth.

It was only after Galileo, Copernicus, Kepler and Newton made their painstaking and inspired discoveries in order to explain the magic of the motion of planets in terms of laws that worked on the earth, that the heavens were looked at with a scientific eye.

The beginning of the twentieth century saw important discoveries in science. The structure of the atom was explained, as also what happens when atoms emitted light. It was also found out that the pressure and temperature of a gas arose from atoms and molecules. With this new knowledge and with improvements in the quality and power of telescopes, scientists began to seriously examine the processes taking place in the sun and the stars, and the discipline of astrophysics took on a new life. It was in this exciting period that Meghnad Saha, of Kolkata University, did important work that helped to establish the sound theoretical foundations of astrophysics.

By the beginning of the twentieth century, the stars, including the sun, were thought to have been formed by the action of gravity between the billions of atoms in a vast cloud of gas, mostly hydrogen. As the gas got compressed, under the huge forces drawing everything towards the centre, it heated up to millions of degrees. Under the intense heat, the atoms of hydrogen were squeezed close enough to fuse into helium, with the release of immense energy. The intense nuclear fire impelled expansion again, till the gas cooled, was compressed again, and so on.

Over the ages, this process of atoms getting squeezed close together resulted in the creation of the heavier elements too. All these elements have been detected in the sun and the stars. How do we detect the presence of an element in a star? It is done by examining the light that comes from the star and looking for the telltale signs of the element in the spectrum of the light, something like the element's fingerprints!

Atoms of the elements consist of a heavy core, which has positively charged protons. The cone is surrounded by a cloud of an equal number of negatively charged electrons. The electrons are very small and could be thought of as orbiting the core, like the planets orbit the sun.

The electrons are distributed in 'shells' around the nucleus. How many electrons go in each shell is determined by certain rules. An important rule is that the outermost shell can have no more than eight electrons. If the element has an additional electron, the electron starts a new shell with one electron, and so on. Atoms also strive to have two or eight electrons in the outer shell. How can they do this? Well, in chemical combination, an element with three electrons in the outer shell may 'lend' an electron to another element with seven in the outer shell, so that they both attain two and eight in the outer shell. But as the number of electrons is now different from the charge on the nucleus, the atom would be charged, or in a state of ionization.

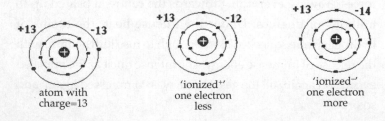

atom with
charge=13

'ionized+'
one electron
less

'ionized−'
one electron
more

All electrons in shells have energies, which keep them in their shells, and away from the nucleus that attracts them. As electrons in the outer shells have been drawn further away from the nucleus, these electrons have more energy than electrons in the inner shells. Electrons can also be temporarily promoted to higher shells, by being given some energy through some form of punch—say, for example, the impact of a particle of light with the energy that separates the two shells. This higher energy state is a temporary one and the atoms would spontaneously de-excite, by emitting a photon, or particle of light, of exactly the energy difference between the two states.

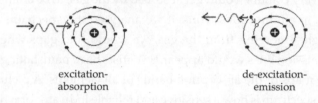

excitation-
absorption

de-excitation-
emission

It is this energy difference between shells, characteristic for each atom, which decides the particular wavelength or colour of the light that the atom emits. These colours emitted by everyday elements can be easily seen. For instance, sodium has a characteristic yellow emission, which we can see just by sprinkling some common salt (sodium chloride) on to the gas flame. If we sprinkled some chalk, instead, we would see a red flame. This is because chalk is calcium carbonate and red is the colour characteristic of calcium. The heat of the flame creates the easiest excitation of the atoms and shows only the colours of basic transitions. Many more colours that are characteristic get emitted with more vigorous excitation of the atoms, like in an electric arc or through sparking.

The light emitted by all elements, under excitation, has been analysed by using sensitive prisms, which split the light up into its constituents. In the case of sunlight, which has all the colours, the spectrum is a series of continuous bands of light. But in the emission from atoms, only specific colours are present and the spectrum is a set of lines, each line representing the characteristic wavelength of the light wave.

Just as atoms can emit light at these characteristic colours by de-exciting, they also absorb light at these same colours to get excited. Thus, if white light, which has all the colours, is shone through a gas of a substance that has particular emission lines, these very colours would get absorbed by the gas, to be emitted again, in all directions. Thus, if we analysed the spectrum of the light emerging from the gas, we would find gaps where the emission lines would appear. Scientists have painstakingly made maps of the absorption bands of all elements. A picture of the spectrum is now a sensitive and reliable indicator of what elements are present in the medium through which any light has come.

The emission and absorption spectra from stars thus become important investigation tools, which reveal details of the structure of the sun, and help refine our understanding.

Apart from this emission of light at particular wavelengths due to de-excitation of electrons, hot objects also emit a continuous spectrum, because of the vibration of their constituent parts. This is the nature of the white light that the sun radiates from its visible part, the photosphere. But when the spectrum of this light is studied in detail, it is seen that the spectrum is crossed by black lines! This is because elements in the outer atmosphere of the sun have absorbed the particular colours. This kind of analysis has shown that the sun contains all the elements that are known on the earth and that almost all stars are also made of the same elements as our sun!

Coming back to the structure of the sun, it was considered, as we had said, to be a gas, compressing itself under its own gravitational pressure, which was compensated by the impulse to expand, because of the heat generated at the core. The behaviour was thus like our own atmosphere, with the pressure due to the atmosphere being greater as nearer the core and less at the periphery. The temperature, also, would be greater nearer the core and less at the periphery.

It is now accepted that the structure of the sun consists of a very hot core, fuelled by nuclear reactions, surrounded by an intermediate region of turbulence and convection currents. Outside this region is the photosphere, the region that we can see. Beyond the photosphere is the chromosphere, a region of thin gas, and yet beyond that is the corona. These outer regions are normally not visible because of the dazzle of the photosphere and it is only during a total solar eclipse that these can be glimpsed.

During an eclipse, the moon's disc covers the bright photosphere and allows the comparatively less intense outer regions to be viewed or photographed. In the normal case, what we see is the absorption spectrum of the chromosphere. But in an eclipse, with the photosphere cut off, we are able to see emission wavelengths of the photosphere and this is most revealing!

During what is called 'flash photography' of the chromosphere and corona, in the short minutes that they are visible, a remarkable discovery was made. They showed the higher energy emission spectrum of calcium, an element forty times as heavy as hydrogen, but no emission spectrum of hydrogen itself. And there were many other elements whose absorption spectra were missing in the chromosphere! It is possible to map the spectrum of different parts of the chromosphere and it was seen that hydrogen seemed to be present till a height of about 8,000 km, but calcium was there at 14,000 km. And furthermore, the lines of calcium seen at this high altitude were the higher energy emissions, which were expected only at higher temperatures!

The discovery confounded the community of astrophysics. How could the heavier calcium be present at higher altitudes than hydrogen? And how could the temperature seem to increase as one moved away from the central source of the heating? Like scientists the world over, Meghnad Saha, then at Kolkata University, was also seized of the problem. Due to his background in the theory of chemical reactions and the subject of thermodynamics, he now was able to formulate an important and new idea.

Meghnad Saha was born in 1893 in a small village not far from Dhaka, then part of the province of Bengal in British India. The family had limited means and it is thanks to a series of fortunate interventions by relatives and well-wishers that young Meghnad was able to go even beyond primary school. But he was consistently a brilliant student in the village school, the English-medium school in a nearby village and then at Dhaka, where he prepared for entrance to college. At Dhaka, he also received a freeship and a stipend. He, however, lost these benefits for taking part in a demonstration against the British governor, at the age of fourteen. Fortunately, he was able to continue his studies, which included the German language, with other financial aid, till he joined Presidency College in Kolkata at the age of eighteen.

At Kolkata, Meghnad was a classmate of S.N. Bose and P.C. Mahalanobis, who became celebrated scientists, and one of his teachers was J.C. Bose himself. Meghnad had a scintillating college career, but at its end, like so many Indians of the time, he tried to get into the civil service so that he could help his family. Fortunately for physics, Meghnad was not considered to have impeccable political credentials and he ended up in Kolkata University with S.N. Bose, thanks to Sir Ashutosh Mukherjee.

In the physics department of the university, S.N. Bose and Saha strove to introduce the latest topics into the curriculum. The two were ultimately given a special allowance and assigned subjects to read up and master, Saha's being quantum theory. Saha's knowledge of German came in very handy, and with the help of books and journals, Bose and Saha were soon up to date with the latest in the world of physics and started actively pursuing research at Kolkata University. In 1920, soon after he joined the university, Saha published his celebrated paper, 'On Ionization in the Solar Chromosphere', which was published in the *Philosophical Magazine*, Cambridge. It dealt with the anamolous radiation seen in the flash photographs of the chromosphere.

To recapitulate, the puzzle in the study of the sun was, how did the upper chromosphere show the highest energy parts of the calcium emission spectrum, although lower parts, where the temperature should have been higher, did not? Did this imply that the sun's atmosphere got hotter as one went higher? And why, in this higher part of the chromosphere, were many other elements absent? And finally, how was it that calcium, forty times heavier than hydrogen, was present at much greater heights?

Explanations had been attempted, and workarounds had been tried, but the problem remained, particularly the one of higher temperatures at greater altitudes. Saha's revolutionary explanation was that the high-energy spectrum was not due to higher temperatures but because the atoms themselves were ionized at higher altitudes.

Ionization consists of separating an electron from the stable configuration of the neutral atom. This requires the use of energy, which again is nothing but raising the gas to higher temperatures. Did Saha's notion of ionization then amount to the same thing as heating? This is where Saha was able to draw on his familiarity with the dynamics of chemical reactions and work out a way for ionization to be possible even with lower temperatures.

In chemistry, many reactions can take place in either direction, depending on conditions. For example, one reaction is when carbon dioxide reacts with hydrogen to produce carbon monoxide and water. Chemists put it like this:

$$CO_2 + H_2 \rightarrow CO + H_2O.$$

But the opposite is also possible, with carbon monoxide and water vapour giving carbon dioxide and hydrogen, like this:

$$CO + H_2O \rightarrow CO_2 + H_2.$$

In fact, in this reaction, there is always a mixture of the four components, with both reactions taking place all the time, the extent of progress of one or the other depending on the temperature and pressure.

Saha pictured the ionized atoms in a similar way. As there were normal atoms, ionized ones and electrons all milling together, he imagined that they may keep exchanging each others' roles. Neutral atoms would break up into ions and ions would combine with electrons to become neutral atoms again. This is rather like the example of carbon dioxide and water vapour given above. And as in the case of the gases, atoms and ions too settled down to an average state of so many ions and so many atom, according to the pressure and the temperature.

And by thinking it out like this, Saha arrived at the celebrated Saha Ionization Formula. The formula showed that ionization increased when the gas got hotter and also when the pressure got less. Now, as one gets higher into the atmosphere of the sun, the temperature falls, but the pressure also decreases. It turns out that the drop in ionization because of the cooling down is less than the increase in ionization because of the drop in the pressure. The result is that the atoms are more ionized higher in the sun's atmosphere, just like the experiments showed, and as illustrated in the diagram below.

So far, the mystery had been: How could the ionization be

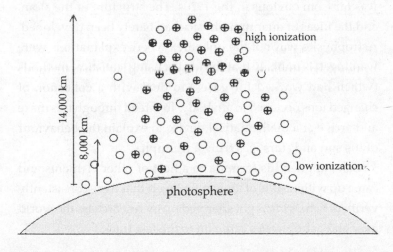

greater at higher altitudes? Did it get hotter as one moved higher? But Saha's formula showed that pressure played a role too, and it was the drop in pressure that did the trick.

Another question to be answered was why there was no emission from some elements at the upper reaches of the sun's atmosphere. This was explained by another part of the formula, which said that the ionization also depended on how much energy it took for an atom to get ionized. If the energy needed was low enough, the atoms got ionized even at low altitudes, where the pressure was large. Elements which had low ionization energies thus got fully ionized long before they reached higher altitudes and then could not emit their characteristic lines.

The Saha Ionization Formula has other interesting features. It helped understand the mechanisms operating in the atmosphere of the sun and the stars, and paved the way for further research and discovery.

On the face of it, it may appear that Saha's thinking was simple and straightforward, but this simple line of thought was far from obvious in the 1920s. The structure of the atom, and the ideas of quantum physics had barely been developed. Astrophysics was not the only area where explanations were wanting. It is unlikely that the idea of using statistical methods (which had worked for gases) to deal with a collection of changed ions occurred to anybody. To thread through this maze and arrive at a mathematical device to explain the behaviour of the sun and stars was truly a triumph.

Saha applied his formula to a host of other elements and came up with results of ionization levels that were consistently verified. Saha's ideas got snapped up by researchers the world over and astrophysics came on to the fast track.

In 1923, Saha became professor of physics at Allahabad University and in 1927 he was elected a fellow of the Royal Society. At Allahabad, and later as the Palit professor at Kolkata, he continued to do research in new areas, like complex spectra, the physics of the atmosphere, and even river physics.

When he came to Kolkata in1938 as the Palit professor, he began to indulge his interest, aroused by a trip abroad in 1937, in nuclear physics and set the ball rolling for a sophisticated piece of equipment called the cyclotron. He started some work in cosmic ray research in Darjeeling and then founded the Saha Insitute of Nuclear Physics, in Kolkata. Nuclear physics was taught as a separate subject in Kolkata University from 1940. The Saha Institute is now a leading research institute and has trained innumerable men of science.

Saha also interested himself in public life, economic planning, and social causes. He was elected an independent member of Parliament from north-west Kolkata, in 1952. He combined his work at the Saha Institute with public life right to the end. He died in 1956, collapsing en route to a meeting in the office of the Planning Commission at New Delhi.

S. CHANDRASEKHAR

THE BLACK HOLE—A REGION OF space where the gravitational forces are so great that even light is not able to escape—is surely one of the most spectacular phenomena of modern astrophysics. The word has become a metaphor for something final, inexorable, from which there were no comebacks. Modern astronomy, using X-rays which can be detected only above the earth's atmosphere, has found evidence of real black holes tucked away in distant galaxies. But what is remarkable is that long before they were detected in experiment, black holes were conceived of in pure theory, thanks to the persistence, in the face of much opposition, of Subrahmanyan Chandrasekhar, then a mere postdoctoral student at Cambridge.

Stars are understood to be born when the material in vast clouds of gas, mostly hydrogen, began to collapse into itself, because of attraction due to gravity. As the cloud grew smaller, it warmed, much like the air in a bicycle pump heats up on being compressed. The temperatures rose to millions of degrees. Nuclear reactions, mostly of hydrogen nuclei combining to form helium, were sparked off. This caused more heat. The heat increased the pressure, which began to resist and then overcame the inward force of gravity. The cloud then expanded, under the force due to the fire in the centre, and kept expanding till the nuclear reactions in the core began to stop. When this happened, the internal pressure began to fall and gravity took over again. In the compression that followed, more energetic nuclear reactions took place, to produce heat and heavier elements still. This again led to expansion, followed by compression, and so on.

When the star is at its largest, with the centre burning but dimly, the star temperature is low and it appears large and reddish, as a red giant. When the star is compressed, with the centre burning vigorously, it is smaller and hotter, with its colour more to the blue side of the spectrum. The bulk of the stars in the heavens, like our sun, are at this stage. Our own sun, too, will grow to be a red giant some day, when its dimensions will engulf the orbit of Saturn, now at a distance of 1.4 billion km from the sun in its present size.

After several such cycles, the nuclear fuel is spent, and there is nothing to counter the gravitational force and the star collapses. The star gets smaller and the force of gravity at the surface gets stronger. But does the star get smaller without limit and reduce to a point? What would be the density of all the matter in the star so compressed? And is this the fate of a star, ultimately to disappear?

By the time these questions were raised, the quantum nature of energy and the wave nature of matter had been understood and a way was seen out of such 'collapse to a point'. A consequence of the quantum theory is that there is a limit to how accurately we can measure the position and the motion of a particle at the same time. For instance, if we spot and locate an electron at rest, we are, in fact, spotting the electron with the help of a photon, or particle of light, which is bouncing off the electron. Now, in this bouncing off of the photon, the electron would recoil and be set in motion. We then have the position of the electron, but the electron is no longer at rest. One way to reduce the recoil would be to use a 'low-energy' photon. But the laws of optics are such that with low-energy photons, we do not get a sharp image, only a blurred one, which leaves the position uncertain. Thus, measurement of the position and the speed of a particle in nature is always a trade-off in the accuracy of either measurement.

The implication of this 'principle of uncertainty' for the collapsing star is that when the particles get squeezed closer together, nature imposes on them an extent of motion, as a result of the reducing scope for uncertainty of position. In a gas, it is the motion of the molecules that causes the pressure of the gas. In the case of the collapsed star too, this motion imposed by the principle of uncertainty gives rise to pressure—even after all the heat is dissipated. This pressure counterbalances the compression by gravity. This concept explains why the collapsing star does not undergo the physically untenable reduction to a geometric point. Instead, the star survives as a highly compressed, hence very hot entity. The dying star thus shines with a nearly white light, and is called the white dwarf.

This was where the theory pertaining to the evolution of stars stood when S. Chandrasekhar graduated from Presidency College, Chennai, in 1929. Chandrasekhar was the nephew of the celebrated C.V. Raman and was a phenomenal student. While still an undergraduate, he had taught subjects far beyond even his teachers' comprehension.

The subject of stars and their development had gripped him early and he had already read the classic, *The Internal Constitution of the Stars*, by Sir Arthur Eddington. Eddington, considered the founder of astrophysics, was known for his work on stellar evolution and for his exposition of Einstein's General Theory of Relativity.

Even while in college, Chandrasekhar had taught himself the new mechanics applicable to the world of the very small, where quantum effects became important. Chandrasekhar had learnt this subject from *Atomic Structure and Spectral Lines* the book by Arnold Sommerfeld, who had applied the methods to the atom. In 1918, Chandrasekhar also had the fortune of meeting with Sommerfeld, who advised Chandrasekhar what else to read. Chandrasekhar went on to publish two research papers while still an undergraduate.

In 1930, Chandrasekhar set out for England to study at Cambridge. And during the two-weeks voyage, he did much of the work that led him to an extraordinary discovery.

The pressure inside a star is related to many features of the star, such as the size, the rate of nuclear reactions in the core, the brightness of the star, and colour. Only the last two features, the brightness and colour, which suggest the temperature, can be seen from the earth. The pressure then needs to be calculated from a theoretical relationship between the parameters.

By 1930, there was a great mass of data about the colour and brightness of stars, plotted in different charts in an effort to find patterns. The methods of mathematical physics had considered what might be the behaviour of the interior of stars, to find a relation that fit the facts. And the work was still in progress. During the voyage to England, Chandrasekhar could not stop thinking about the problem of white dwarfs.

The atoms that make up a normal star consist of a positive nucleus, surrounded by negatively charged electrons. The atoms are thus electrically neutral and behave like billiard balls in motion, moving faster and pushing out to expand when compressed or heated. But at the fantastic pressures in white dwarfs, this picture of neutral atoms like billiard balls would not hold, as the atoms would all have split up into positive nuclei and negative electrons. There would then be two gases of charged particles with huge forces of attraction and repulsion, and new rules of quantum mechanics of how they distributed their total energy among themselves.

During his voyage, Chandrasekhar attempted a rigorous application of all this to the case of the white dwarf and came up with a solution that bristled with problems! If the equations were applied to a white dwarf of low mass, they behaved well enough and gave solutions which fit nicely with the data. But when the mass of the star increased beyond a point, the equations themselves became unsolvable. Something in the problem or in the way the solution was being attempted led to features that did not make sense!

The questions raised during the two weeks on the ship stayed with Chandrasekhar for many years. At Cambridge he showed his calculations to Professor Fowler, whose work he had read while in India. Professor Fowler, in fact, was the first to have seen that quantum-mechanical effects would show up in white dwarfs, but he did not consider the way things changed when the mass increased beyond a point to be significant. Chandrasekhar could not divine where the problem could lie, but it is clear that he could not let go the conviction that there was something remarkable hiding down there!

Chandrasekhar received his Ph.D in 1933 and also a fellowship at Trinity College. He continued his work on white dwarfs. He now believed that apart from quantum effects, the results of Einstein's Theory of Relativity would also be relevant to the problem. Einstein's Special Theory, set out in 1905, had shown that our ideas about space and time, which work quite well in daily life, break down at speeds approaching the speed of light. At these speeds, time seems to move slower and lengths seem to contract. Mass seems to increase and even speeds do not add up in the usual way. The theory shows that energy and mass are equivalent to each other and things get more massive as they move faster. Chandrasekhar saw that at the densities in white dwarfs, the speeds involved would be nearly that of light and so he worked the implications of the Theory of Relativity into the calculations.

Chandrasekhar worked out a mathematical expression for the pressure in the star, in terms of the various parameters, after taking the quantum-mechanical and the relativistic effects carefully into account. The resulting expression had important differences from the earlier ones arrived at by Fowler and Chandrasekhar himself. These earlier results had worked well when the density was low and the effects of relativity were not significant. Chandrasekhar's new formulation also gave the same results in the low-density scenario. To get a quick look at how the relation behaved in the high-density case, Chandrasekhar tried out what happened when the density was considered to be infinitely high. Normally, mathematical relations do not make a lot of sense if a parameter is put at infinity. For example, the acceleration of an object falling under gravity is given by the force of gravity divided by its mass. Now, if the mass is put to infinity, the force of gravity also becomes infinite. And the acceleration, which is the quotient of two infinites, is quite uncertain.

But what Chandrasekhar found was that even with density set to infinity, the relation he had developed made sense, provided the mass of the star was at least 1.4 times the mass of the sun! This was amazing. As infinite density means zero volume, it suggests that if a star with a mass 1.4 times the mass of the sun runs out of fuel, it would shrink to a point!

Chandrasekhar worked on this result for months on end and presented his work to many of his illustrious colleagues. None of them seemed to think there was anything in it. But Chandrasekhar soon grew convinced that high-mass white dwarfs could not exist. The state of a low-mass white dwarf was a balance between gravitational forces and the pressure due to the charged particles being squeezed together. If matter like asteroids and comets washing in caused the mass of the star to gradually increase, the force of gravity also increases, with the pressure also changing in a complex way. As the mass increases, the balance between the two forces gets less stable, till, at the limiting mass, now known as the Chandrasekhar limit, the balance breaks down, rather like a truck tipping over as the platform on which it stands is gradually tilted!

The result could also be understood in the context of a conclusion that had been drawn from Einstein's General Theory of Relativity. Einstein had shown that the measures of position, speed and even time intervals are related to how fast one observer was moving in relation to another. The theory showed that moving measures seemed to get shorter and even intervals of time got stretched when viewed in a moving frame. When events were plotted not with the usual three dimensions that we are used to, but with a fourth dimension for time, the time intervals reduced to the same even for moving observers. And then, the theory showed that energy and mass were equivalent, with the famous $E=mc^2$ relation.

When dealing with acceleration caused by gravity of objects with mass, the theory was generalized first to treat gravity and acceleration as the same thing. As mass caused inertia and acceleration, it became possible to regard mass itself as a geometric property of space. Once viewed like this, it was not the path of a planet around a star that was curved, but space itself was curved around the massive star! This would mean that even light should move in a curved path around a large mass. This has been verified during the solar eclipse, when the stars become visible. The stars just behind the sun's disk should still be blocked out. But it is found that stars in the periphery of the disk are still visible, as if light has reached us by curving around the sun!

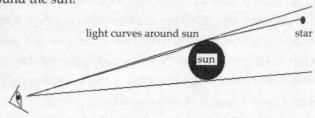

light curves around sun   star

sun

Using these principles, Karl Schwarzschild had found that if an object were to shrink small enough, it could be so dense as to curve space in its vicinity so that no light could escape. The size at which this would happen for an object was called its Schwarzschild radius. And for Chandrasekhar's collapsed star, one view could be that the star had reduced to its Schwarzschild radius.

For all that, so amazing and difficult to digest was Chandrasekhar's result that just nobody who mattered in the 1930s was willing to give it a second thought. The force of gravity at the surface of the entity that Chandrasekhar predicted would be so great that objects falling in would approach the speed of light. The leading edge of the object would accelerate faster than the trailing end and the object would get stretched out. And still, for an object reaching the tremendous speeds, time would come to a virtual standstill and it would take an eternity before it reached the surface.

Eddington openly lashed out at the young Chandrasekhar and many other sympathetic colleagues tried to reason with him. But a reading of the comments and critiques of these savants reveals statements which hardly have the kind of solid logic needed to counter cold mathematics. 'I think there should be a law of nature to prevent a star from behaving in this absurd way,' said Eddington. 'It is clear that matter cannot behave as you predict,' said E.A. Milne, scientist and Chandrasekhar's friend. Even the Russian physicist, Lev Landau, who two year later independently arrived at the same expression as Chandrasekhar, could not accept matter reducing to zero dimensions and said, 'Stars heavier than the limit (that the theory showed) should have regions where the laws of quantum mechanics are violated.'

Rather than beat his head against the wall, Chandrasekhar put down his findings about the structure of stars in a book that would to influence, more than Eddington's remarks could, subsequent developments in the field. Chandrasekhar went to work on a new area—stellar dynamics. After a time, he wrote a comprehensive tome on that and shifted his attention to other fields. And so he went on, leaving an indelible mark on each field he took up, in a manner that few have equalled.

Chandrasekhar's book on the structure of stars, *Introduction to the Study of Stellar Structures*, was published in 1937. In the years that followed, the evolution of stars was intensely tracked using painstaking calculations. In some of the cases, but only a few, the stars were found to explode before they collapsed to a point. But the possibility of collapse was distinctly gaining acceptance.

In 1967 came the discovery of pulsars. Pulsars were sources of regular radio pulses that came often from the centre of brilliantly lit nebulae or clouds—the remains of stars that had violently exploded. These were first thought of as signals from intelligent beings in outer space, but were soon recognized as coming from collapsing white dwarfs. As the star collapsed, the core was crushed so hard that electrons and protons merged to form neutrons, with release of energy. The energy blew off the outer parts of the star while the neutron core collapsed into the densest matter known. The tremendous gravity as well as magnetic fields in the vicinity of the core accelerated matter to emit light and X-rays, which illuminated the surrounding debris of the explosion. The neutron core itself rotated and emitted radio waves or X-rays, rather like a lighthouse, seen as pulse every time it pointed our way.

The discovery of this neutron core of a collapsed star was a first, exciting instance of an entity suggested by the productions for heavier stars. But what of the black hole itself? This was where a star many times the mass of the sun ended up when its fuel was over, unlike smaller stars that indeed as white dwarfs or exploded and left a neutron core. What could be the method to find a thing a few kilometres across and which emitted no light?

It was X-ray astronomy that made it possible. X-ray astronomy, conducted above the atmosphere with the help of rockets and satellites, revealed an astonishing richness of images in the X-rays pouring in from the heavens. Because the earth's atmosphere is opaque to X-rays (and a good thing, too!) this whole area of astronomy was blocked from view till we learnt to launch telescopes above the atmosphere. A number of neutron stars were now detected, radiating in pulses, but in the X-ray region. Many of these were seen to have paired with a larger, regular star, with the pair spinning, like a tumbling dumb-bell. Such pairs are known as binary stars. This, in fact, was detected because the periodicity of the pulses rose and fell, as the neutron star was moving away from us or towards us, as it whirled around with its companion.

But if the heavier partner in the pair is a black hole, the companion feels so great a pull that the tidal forces begin to suck matter right out. And so fast does this matter move, as it rushes towards the black hole, that it heats up to millions of degrees and begins to radiate X-rays. It is by looking for these X-rays, in places where such pairs are expected—with the telltale effects of the wobbling of the source of the X-rays, but with no pulses—that the presence of a black hole can be inferred.

X-ray astronomy and the study of the interiors of stars are now pursued by hundreds of scientists, with huge funding. Hundreds of white dwarfs, brown dwarfs, nebulae, all kinds of X-ray sources, have been photographed and studied. In the 1960s and 1970s, hundreds of 'candidate black holes' were detected, and in many cases, the evidence is now overwhelming that they are, in fact, authentic black holes.

Chandrasekhar received twenty honorary degrees, was elected to twenty-one learned societies and received numerous awards including the Nobel Prize in 1982 for his work on the evolution of stars, which had initially received so much ridicule from peers and journals in England. Other honours included the Gold Medal of the Royal Astronomical Society of London; the Rumford Medal of the American Academy of Arts and Sciences; the Royal Medal of the Royal Society, London; the

National Medal of Science; and the Henry Draper Medal of the National Academy of Sciences.

For his whole life he worked in the area of stellar dynamics, and was a dedicated teacher. Many of his students, in fact, received the Nobel before him!

He was a man of diverse interests especially literature, music and the philosophy of science. He lectured frequently on the relationship between the arts and the sciences, and also expounded on this at length in his book *Truth and Beauty: Aesthetics and Motivations in Science*.

He died in Chicago in 1995. As a mark of respect, the most sophisticated X-ray observatory to date, launched by the Columbia in 1999, was fittingly named Chandra.

Homi Bhabha

In 1947, WHEN INDIA BECAME INDEPENDENT, science and technology were things that belonged to another world. India was largely underdeveloped and rural, the little technology that one could see was imported, and one had to go abroad for higher education. That India today has risen to become a nation with a vigorous nuclear power programme and research institutes that rival the best in the world is testimony to the rare ability and vision substantially of one man.

Homi Jehangir Bhabha combined the skills of a first-rate scientist with the capacity to dream and then translate dreams to reality. In nineteen short years, from 1947 to 1966, Bhabha established the Tata Institute of Fundamental Research (TIFR) in Mumbai, the research centre at Trombay, now known as the Bhabha Atomic Research Centre (BARC), the Centre for Advanced Research in Chennai, and the Centre for Advanced Technology at Indore. And he laid the solid foundations of a gamut of activities within the nuclear programme, from prospecting for nuclear ores to feeding electricity from fully operational nuclear power plants to the national grid.

H.J. Bhabha was born in 1909 in a Parsi family of great culture and learning. He was brought up in Mumbai and educated in the European tradition, in the arts and in music as well as in the sciences, in which Bhabha displayed early interest. By the time he was sixteen, he had studied the Special Theory of Relativity, then barely familiar even to the well-educated. After school he continued at the Elphinstone College and then the Royal Institute of Science, both of which were in Mumbai. At eighteen, Bhabha left for England and joined Gonville and Caius College at Cambridge. Bhabha took his Tripos, first in mechanical engineering in deference to his father's wish, and then in mathematics, in 1932, to fulfil his own dreams.

For the next seven years, while he completed his Ph.D, Bhabha had a series of fellowships. These enabled him to work with the leading physicists of the time, including Wolfgang Pauli and Enrico Fermi, and at the best institutes, like the Bohr Institute at Copenhagen.

In 1939, Bhabha returned to India for a short break, but World War II broke out before he could go back to England. In England, many scientists joined the war effort and basic research was not the priority. Bhabha decided to stay in India and accepted a readership at the Indian Institute of Science, Bangalore. With the help of a small grant from a Tata trust, Bhabha set up a unit to start work on cosmic rays.

Bhabha had got interested in cosmic rays while at Cambridge and he ploughed into the field with enthusiasm. Cosmic rays were a mysterious radiation that seemed to come from outer space. They interacted strongly with the upper atmosphere and hardly any of the rays reached the earth's surface. It was later discovered that cosmic rays were largely protons, or the positively charged particles in the nuclei of atoms, probably produced by stars and in supernova explosions. These particles interacted with atoms in the atmosphere and gave rise to 'secondaries' that consisted of a variety of elementary particles.

Cosmic ray particles are detected by using the principle that a charged particle streaking through a gas would knock electrons out of the atoms of the gas and create charged ions. If there were plates that were connected to a powerful battery on either side of the gas, the ions would conduct electricity and cause a pulse of current. Counting the pulses would then be a count of cosmic rays passing through. To count particles coming in a given direction, one could place a series of such detectors in a row along that direction. If all detectors showed a pulse together, that would be a count of a particle that had come through all of them.

Another device for detecting cosmic rays was the cloud chamber. This was a container which would show tracks of charged particles, rather like the vapour trails that jet aircraft produce in the sky. The cloud chamber allowed the tracks to be photographed and also revealed the results of a collision, when one occurred within the chamber. As the particles were charged, they curved and deflected in magnetic and electric fields. Having such fields enabled identification of the charge on the particles by seeing which way they curved.

Bhabha soon created a formidable research facility at the Indian Institute of Science, using innovation and improvization where funds or equipment were wanting. But by 1944, he felt the need for a larger facility and approached the Tata trusts again. As the war appeared to be reaching an end, there was also the possibility of returning to England. He, however, wrote in a letter to J.R.D. Tata in 1943 that he could continue to stay in the country and see if suitable conditions could be created, of 'doing one's duty to one's country and building up schools comparable with those in other lands.'

The Sir Dorab Tata Trust responded to Bhabha's proposal and the TIFR was born in Bangalore in 1945. A few months later, the Institute was shifted to Mumbai, working out of a building which was owned by an aunt of Bhabha.

Talented persons gravitated to TIFR and Bhabha soon had a remarkable team at work. By 1949, the premises grew cramped and they moved to a picturesque building near the Gateway of India. The work involved research in cosmic rays and mathematics. International conferences were held and the world's leading scientists were regular visitors. As the problem of space cropped up again, in 1962, the Institute moved to its present location, at the southern tip of the Mumbai island.

The Institute is now a vigorous centre of committed research in a variety of frontier areas in physics and mathematics. It has facilities for experimental work, including those in the hill resort of Pachmarhi in Madhya Pradesh and in the gold mines at Kolar in Karnataka. A sizeable branch is at Bangalore, dedicated to research in the biological sciences.

The tradition of order, organization, commitment and dedication that Bhabha inculcated into TIFR during the time he guided its affairs has survived. Today, the Institute is a model for others to emulate. The work done is of the highest order and its colloquia and seminars attract the best in the world.

A great development of the times when Bhabha started work in India was the possibility of harnessing immense energy from the splitting of atomic nuclei. Einstein had already formulated his celebrated equation $E=mc^2$ (where E is the energy, m is the mass and c is the speed of light), or the equivalence of mass and energy, and discoveries had been made about the nuclei of atoms.

The nuclei of atoms consist of positively charged protons and about the same number of electrically neutral particles called neutrons. The act of holding together a number of such particles takes energy. It is found that the total mass of such a nucleus is a tiny bit *less* than the total of the mass of each of the constituents—the difference being the mass which is equivalent to the binding energy. In some heavier nuclei, it is found that the nucleus could be more economically packed as two smaller nuclei. Economical, that is, in the use of binding energy. If the nucleus could be split into these smaller parts, the saving in binding energy would be released. And this energy could be used to set off an explosion, or to drive a turbine in a power plant.

It is like having a pair of golf balls in a golf hole at the top of a mound. The golf balls together are in a higher energy state than when separate, on the fairway. If the balls were pushed out of the hole, using a little energy, they would roll down the slope and release a good deal more energy!

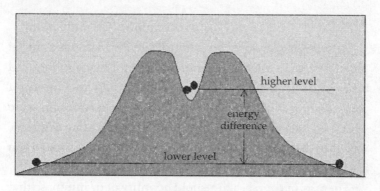

Uranium, which is about the heaviest of natural elements, has two forms of its nucleus. Both forms have 92 protons, but while one form has 143 neutrons, the other has 146 neutrons. As it is the protons that decide the chemical properties of an element, both forms are uranium. But the different numbers of neutrons make for slightly different 'packaging economies'. These forms are called U_{235} and U_{238}—the subscripts being the total number of particles in the nucleus—and are central to the design of nuclear reactors.

Both forms of uranium are found to split up, or 'fission', either naturally or on being struck by a stray neutron. The natural fission is very slow, but in both cases, there is release of huge energy. The energy released by fission of one gram of uranium, for instance, is about a million times the heat obtained from burning a gram of coal, more like burning a tonne of coal! But it is the specific way that U_{235} breaks up, when struck by a neutron, that makes possible the nuclear chain reaction.

The way U_{235} breaks up can be shown like this:

$$U_{235} + n \rightarrow Sr_{94} + Xe_{139} + 3n \text{ [Strontium and Xenon]}$$

or

$$U_{235} + n \rightarrow Br_{87} + La1_{47} + 2n \text{ [Bromine and Lanthanum]}$$

In both the reactions the products are the 'daughter' nuclei plus three or two leftover neutrons. That a reaction induced by a neutron results in neutrons again has an important consequence. If just one nucleus in a mass of uranium were struck by a chance neutron, this would produce more neutrons, which, in their turn, would induce more fissions, and so on! In a fraction of a second, all the nuclei would fission.

There is, of course, a threshold quantity of uranium, so that the 'daughter' neutrons do not get wasted and the chain is kept going. In pure or natural uranium, which has only 0.6 per cent of U_{235}, this quantity is about ninety kg. But even much smaller quantities get unbearably hot and give off radiation.

Apart from this ominous scope for destruction by plunging quantities of fissile material together, Enrico Fermi had also discovered the possibility of a *controlled* fission reaction, which could be used to generate power. In this method, portions of the fuel are not allowed to come close enough for a runaway reaction but are kept separated by shields of lead or graphite, which absorb neutrons and slow things down. The result is only generation of heat, which could be siphoned off by a circulating coolant and used for driving turbines.

Bhabha saw at once the promise of atomic power to fuel the development of free India. It was audacious to think that a country without enough to eat and barely able to produce cement and steel for basic civil construction should dream of harnessing newborn technology as a short cut to industry and growth. But Bhabha was a visionary and his comprehension of science and its relation with life went beyond the academic.

This was the year 1947. The war was just over, Independence was at hand and a regular government was yet to be formed. Bhabha did not think it proper to wait. He convinced Pandit Nehru, then leader of the interim government, that despite all the political and economic priorities of a country newly free, development of atomic energy capability could not afford to be delayed. In the months that followed Independence, even during the turmoil of Partition, Bhabha was able to set up an independent government agency—the Atomic Energy Commission—to take on the first needs of prospecting for nuclear energy ores and funding basic research. Soon, the development of a full-fledged programme was put in the hands of a specially empowered department of atomic energy, with Bhabha at its head.

The purification of nuclear materials was still a closely guarded military secret and the technology of controlling nuclear reactions for power generation had hardly made any headway. It was in 1953 that Bhabha's team made its first gram of uranium. The power needs of countries run into thousands of millions of watts (megawatts) and a nuclear programme would have to think of plants that would use tonnes of fuel, with precise controls and meticulous safety, as every nuclear plant had the potential to transform itself into a monster of horrendous destruction.

Basic research being carried out in TIFR was soon shifted to a dedicated facility, the Atomic Energy Establishment (AEE), now known as the Bhabha Atomic Research Centre, then situated just outside Mumbai. The AEE soon grew into a powerhouse of research and development, with its well-planned laboratories, and programmes to train scientists and engineers at the best facilities in the world. There was also the Training School, which recruited fresh graduates and honed them into the experts that the phenomenal growth in activities would demand.

As India had scarce resources of uranium, Bhabha tailored India's nuclear energy programme to make the best of what there was. The thrust was on using natural uranium, the fissile kind, in place of 'enriched uranium', which had a better proportion of U_{235}. The economics of this strategy was that by suitable methods, the natural ore could fuel an initial nuclear energy programme, so long as the supply of ore lasted. This would save the time and expense of creating ore enrichment facilities. A by-product of fission in natural uranium was plutonium, which got generated by the U_{238} present in the fuel. Plutonium is also capable of nuclear chain reaction. By the time the U_{235} got used up, there would thus be a stockpile of plutonium for another spell of power generation.

This possibility arises from the fact that the two or more neutrons that emerge from fission of U_{235}, are too energetic to optimally set off fresh U_{235} fission reactions. They could be more effective if slowed down a bit. The reactor is thus designed to be filled with a moderator, a material that the neutrons can hit en route to striking the U_{235} nuclei. The best moderator is heavy water, a form of water where the nuclei of the hydrogen atoms are heavier than normal hydrogen nuclei. In natural uranium reactors, in fact, heavy water also acts as the coolant and serves to carry away the heat generated in the reactor to be used to generate power in turbines.

Another moderator already present in the natural uranium fuel is U_{238}. High-energy neutrons get slowed down when they bump off U_{238} nuclei, just like with heavy water. This useful function apart, when a nucleus of U_{238} absorbs a neutron, the product is a nucleus with 238+1=239 particles. This is an unstable form of uranium, which spontaneously breaks down into the element plutonium. Plutonium, like U_{235}, also undergoes fission, producing neutrons that could sustain a chain reaction. When the U_{235} is gone, we could continue with a plutonium reactor!

If one stuffed leftover U_{238} into this plutonium reactor, one would get still more plutonium. This kind of reactor could now become a breeder, a reactor that produces more fuel than it consumes.

This was the first step in economizing and making the best of the uranium reserves in the country. There is yet another step. This depends upon thorium, Th_{232}, of which, happily, India has ample reserves. When thorium is exposed to neutrons in a plutonium reactor, it gets transformed into U_{233}, again a fissile material. Phase III of India's atomic energy plan was to generate U_{233} by exposing thorium to neutrons. This phase would last a long time, because of abundant thorium deposits discovered on the Kerala coast.

As early as 1955, at an international conference on atomic energy at Geneva, Bhabha had recognized atomic power as being the practical, long-term answer to the world's energy needs. At the conference, Bhabha had spoken of the next development in nuclear power, nuclear fusion, as being the real holy grail. While nuclear fission is getting power out of the splitting of heavy nuclei into more economical smaller units, nuclear fusion looks to the merging of light nuclei into more complex nuclei, a process that releases even more energy! Specifically, the nuclei of heavy hydrogen, which consist of a proton and a neutron, are forced close together. When they are close enough, nuclear forces which attract each other take over and the nuclei merge, into a nucleus of helium, two protons and two neutrons.

As in the case of fission, in fusion too, energy has first to be supplied to overcome a barrier before it can be tapped when the system crashes down to a low-energy condition. But in the case of fusion, a truly formidable energy input is required. The only way it has been done is in the hydrogen bomb where a normal fission bomb is used to start off the fusion reaction. But, in 1955, Bhabha spoke of the prospects of the process being controlled and harnessed. With the huge quantity of heavy hydrogen in the oceans, mastering fusion would put to an end any concerns about energy.

It was with this confidence and optimism that Bhabha had approached setting up India's atomic energy plan. With the large master plan—going from heavy water reactors to breeders and then using the thorium cycle—in place, Bhabha set about its unfolding in practice. Innumerable details had to be developed, mastered and implemented. A professional prospecting body had to be set up to locate where nuclear ores could be mined. The metals had to be extracted and the content of the useful isotopes improved. The fuel material then had to be shaped and packed, for the tortuous conditions in the reactor.

Reactor design was an uncharted territory, esoteric in theory and exacting in practice. High temperatures and pressures apart, there was the need to contain radiation, as well as to provide for safety in case of mishap. Even the civil structures that housed the facilities had to be specially designed and the plants had to be located far from towns and cities. And then methods had to be devised to dispose of spent fuel.

With uncanny judgement, system and method, Bhabha led and inspired his team to plan and build the wide spectrum of interlocking systems, quite unlike anything in the developing world. But, in 1966, on his way to Vienna for a meeting, he met an untimely and tragic end when the plane he was in crashed into the Alps.

The nation was plunged into despair and the setback seemed impossible to repair. But the ultimate testimony to the organization that Bhabha had created was that it rolled on almost without a break after his death. In a country where it is customary to stop work to mourn the passing of great men, the department of atomic energy worked resolutely on the days following Bhabha's death. Bhabha's grand plan had marked out a clear path and the department followed it with energy and dedication.

India is now self-sufficient in most components of nuclear power. Her heavy water technology, largely indigenous, has captured export markets. Her research establishments are second to few in the world and her backbone of manpower is formidable. Nuclear power is now an important and growing part of the power plan of the country, thanks to the grand vision and untiring effort of one man.

HARGOBIND KHORANA

IN JUST 150 YEARS, THE FIELD of genetics has grown from insignificance to an area that commands the highest respect. Charles Darwin's *On the Origin of Species*, published in 1859, was the first scientific examination of the mystery of inheritance. Today, with the documenting of the human genome, the wonder has been laid bare.

The human genome is the blueprint of the human genetic heritage—billions of units of information stored within the structure of a giant molecule found in every living cell. The story behind the unravelling of the human genome involves the efforts of many scientists in the field of genetic studies. Professor Hargobind Khorana, Nobel laureate, was one of the stars. In order to understand his contribution, however, it is essential to know something about contemporary research.

Before 1859, species were considered unchanging and fixed, desfined to stay as 'God had created them'. Darwin's discovery, that species evolved through natural selection, was based on fossil records and geographical distribution of species. As living conditions like climate, vegetation and food supply underwent changes, certain species began to find themselves less fit to cope. Freak individuals in the species, whose peculiarities proved to be an advantage, were the ones to survive. Over centuries, Darwin's theory propounded, the character of the species itself was changed. This was to suggest that it was a process, rather than God's will, which moulded the species, including the human race. This ran contrary to current theological belief. Darwin, however, made no suggestions as to how the changes in the species might arise.

In the mean time, Gregor Mendel, an Augustinian monk and teacher of high-school students in Austria, discovered important features of heredity. By patiently recording the results of cross-breeding pea plants, Mendel found that the traits passed on by parents to offspring were passed in 'factors' or units—one for each specific trait and with equal contribution by each parent. These hereditary factors did not combine, but were passed intact; each parent transmitting roughly half of its hereditary factors to each offspring. Certain factors were 'dominant' over others and different offspring of the same parents received different sets of hereditary factors.

Mendel's work, published in 1866, had shown that heredity passed through discrete units, which we now call genes. In later years other scientists refined the theory of how genes were inherited, but the nature of the genetic material was still undiscovered.

At about the same time, in 1868, a Swiss biologist called Friedrich Miescher analysed the nuclei of human white cells and found that they consisted of a substance which contained phosphorus. He called it nuclein.

Miescher found that nuclein consisted of an acidic part and a protein part. We now know that the acid part was DNA and the protein part helps package the DNA. But at that time, the possibility that nuclein or nucleic acid could have a role in cell inheritance was just a suspicion, almost dismissed in the face of the seeming lack of chemical diversity in nucleic acids.

Only in 1943 was it shown that it was the nucleic acid in the cell which carried genetic information. Oswald Avery and others at the Rockefeller Institute showed that injecting the nucleic acid from one strain of bacteria into another changed the recipient bacterium into the donor strain. It looked like the genetic component in the material injected was taken up by and became part of the recipient. The study of genetics now made a transition from a 'describing and classifying' subject to an analytical science. The field of molecular biology was born.

In 1952, an experiment was conducted using a radioactive marker to identify individual atoms. It showed that it was indeed the nucleic acid portion of a virus, and not the protein coat, which entered the host cell and provided the genetic information for replication of the virus inside the host. But how this information was carried and expressed was still a great, unanswered question.

How did the contents of one sperm and one egg cell, the sperm invisible and the egg smaller than a full stop in this page, produce a whole human being, different from any other? How did the millions of cells in the human body know what kind of cell they were and what proteins to produce? How could the information to tell a kidney cell it was a kidney cell, or a brain cell what cell it was, be stuffed into the nucleus of the cell?

Much research was conducted on the structure and properties of deoxyribonucleic acid, or DNA, which was the carrier of this genetic information. One fact which was established was that the nucleic acid molecule is a long 'backbone' attached to groups of atoms called 'bases' or 'nucleotide bases'.

The backbone is a regular succession of sugar molecules, separated by phosphate groups, or atoms of phosphorus and

base   base   base

sugar phosphate sugar phosphate sugar

oxygen. The sugar molecules, of course, are hydrocarbons. The structure is like the diagram on the previous page.

A convenient way of visualizing the nucleic acid molecule is like this:

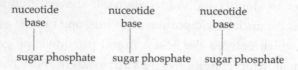

The DNA molecule is built up in this way and has millions of units. Each mammoth DNA molecule forms one threadlike 'chromosome' and there are twenty-three pairs of chromosomes in the nucleus of each human cell. The word 'chromosome' came from the fact that the material in the nucleus could take a coloured stain, for observation, and had been named chromatin. DNA (deoxyribonucleic acid) is named after deoxyribose, the sugar molecule found in the backbone.

The next bit of information was that the bases, to which each nucleic acid molecule was attached, took only four forms, in all the samples of DNA. These forms were adenine (A), guanine (G), thymine (T) and cytosine (C). But these four forms could be present in different proportions in the DNA of different organisms.

An important discovery in the late 1940s was that the quantities of A and T or G and C always turned out to be equal—whenever there was an A, there would be a T, and whenever there was a G, there would be a C. This observation was an important clue to the structure of the DNA and later also to its function.

The last clue that enabled getting at the structure of DNA came from the X-ray studies of Maurice Franklin and Rosalind

Wilkins, in England. Most people are familiar with the use of X-rays to cast shadows of bones, to detect fractures. But X-rays are also useful in science because they consist of waves whose dimensions match the distance between atoms in crystals and molecules. Regular features of molecules are then revealed by patterns in which X-rays passing through the molecules are scattered.

The work of Franklin and Wilkins soon showed that the structure of DNA displayed a 'periodic' nature along its length, one period repeating every 0.34 nm and a secondary one every 3.4 nm (a nanometre, nm, is a millionth of a millimetre).

James Watson and Francis Crick pieced all these clues together: the repeating sugar and phosphate, the A, G, T, C appearing with equal quantities of A and T or G and C, and the periodicities along the length of the molecule. Using a method rather like putting together a three-dimensional jigsaw puzzle, they proposed the celebrated 'double helix' model, of two nucleic acid chains intertwined and connected by links of A and T or G and C (which accounted for there being an A for every T and a G for every C).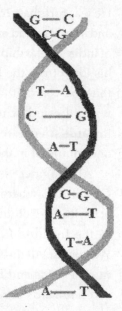

This was a stupendous breakthrough. The two strands being connected by complementary pairs of A-T or G-C makes sure that if the two strands were separated, each half could build up the remaining part by adding exactly an A for every T and a G for every C, and vice versa. During cell division, then, DNA could split and one half could go into each half of the dividing cell. The DNA strands could then rebuild themselves and generate two complete, identical cells. Watson and Crick shared the 1962 Nobel Prize for the discovery.

Hargobind Khorana born in 1922 in an Raipur, obscure village in Punjab in the then undivided India. The youngest of five children of the village patwari, or the clerk who kept land records, Khorana was an unlikely candidate for holding centre stage in the drama that was unfolding. The village itself had a population of about a hundred and Khorana's father was poor. But he had great regard for education and the children were sent to school.

Khorana attended the DAV School in Multan and later went to the Punjab University at Lahore, where he took his M.Sc. He was fortunate to study under gifted teachers both at school and in college and in 1945, Khorana was awarded a Government of India scholarship to go to England for his Ph.D. He completed his Ph.D from the University of Liverpool in 1945 and spent the next year with Professor Vladamir Prelog in Zurich. This was a period when Khorana's thought and philosophy towards science, research and work were strongly influenced and moulded in the European tradition.

After a brief visit to India in 1949, Khorana went back to Cambridge, where he stayed till 1952. He moved on to work at the British Columbia Research Council in Vancouver and then to the Institute for Enzyme Research at the University of Wisconsin. All through, his interest was in the area of proteins, nucleic acids and DNA, and the exciting developments that raced towards unravelling the mystery of heredity.

When Crick and Watson proposed the double helix model in 1953, the framework of transmitting genetic information had been found. Here was a stable mechanism which seemed to have the necessary complexity, as also a method to split in two and yet be able to replicate the original from the separate halves. It was elegant and versatile, but yet, there was no clarity about the code itself. Just how did the chain of A, T, G and C lead to the specific and diverse functions of the billions of cells in a living organism?

The answers to these questions came from the work of Robert Holley, Khorana and Marshall Nirenberg. It had been found by then that the body functions of organisms were controlled by a kind of protein called enzymes, agents that promote the growth of specific things. The colour of a person's eyes, for instance, are the result of a specific enzyme that his body produces, which in turn promotes the production of the dye that leads to the colour of the eyes. Whether a person is diabetic is again a result of chemical agents that determine the rate of production of insulin. And whether these agents are present and in what numbers, depends on the instructions contained in the cells that produce the agents. The individuality of a person, in short was determined by what proteins his body was programmed to produce.

Proteins it had been found, were composed of just twenty building blocks, called amino acids. Amino acids are organic molecules, containing from ten to thirty atoms. Different combinations—sometimes short strings, sometimes thousands of units long—of these twenty components construct all the millions of proteins that are found. Of these twenty, only some can be synthesized by the body and the rest need to be ingested as food. But from this stock of twenty amino acids, the code in the DNA ensures that complicated proteins are constructed. What could be the mechanism that leads to the spelling of particular proteins? Could the combination of the groups that defined each protein be deciphered?

The way the code works is that every three successive nucleotides form the code for either the start of a list of amino acids, an amino acid itself or the end of the list. It is like a long chain of beads, made of beads of just four colours. If we say that a sequence of three reds is the start signal and that three blues is the end signal, we could assign all other combination of red, blue and the other two colours to describe the amino acids. And between each 'start' and 'end', there would be the sequence of amino acids for a protein. In this way, through the millions of nucleotides in the long chain of the DNA molecule, thousands and thousands of sequences of amino acids, each of which defines a protein, get spelt out.

The code that Nirenberg and Khorana deciphered is given in the following page. (The letter U appears for T, because the actual production of amino acids takes place by copying parts of the DNA onto RNA molecules, which have Uracil in place of Thymine.)

So in this way, every consecutive group of three nucleotides, or every 'triad', was the code for a particular amino acid. AUG, code for methionine is the 'start' triad and we can see from the chart that there are three versions of the 'stop' triad. These show where the sequence of amino acids for one protein starts and stops. Each sequence, from 'start' to 'finish', which identifies one protein, is called a 'gene'. And the whole DNA is the code of thousands of proteins. The complement of twenty-three pairs

UUU	phonyl	UCU		UAU	tyrodine	UCU	cyeteine
UUC	alanine	UCC	serine	IIAC		UGC	
UUA		UCA		UAA	stop	UGA	stop
UUC	leucine	UCG		UAG		UGG	tryptophan
CUU		CCU		CAU	nistidine	CGU	
CUC		CCC		CAC		CGC	
CUA	leucine	CCA	proline	CAA		CGA	arginine
CUG		CCG		CAG	alutamine	CCC	
AUU		ACU		AAU	asperagine	AGU	
AUC	isoleucine	ACC	threamine	AAC		AGC	
AUA		ACA		AAA		AGA	serine
AUG	methionine	ACG		AAG	lyoine	AGG	
GUU		GCU		GAU	aspartic acid	GCU	
GUC	valine	GCC	alumina	GAC		GGC	glycine
GUA		GCA		GAA	glutamic acid	GGA	
GUG		GCG		GAG		GGG	

of chromosomes in the human cell then identify all the proteins that determine the complete, individual design, first as a human being and then the individual heritage, of every living person.

From here Nirenberg, Khorana, and Holley went on to do their most important work, which was analysing how exactly the information was tapped and used in formation of proteins.

The entire DNA, it was found, did not participate in formation of proteins. Bits and pieces of the DNA, genes that represent proteins, were copied on to similar molecules called RNA and shipped out of the cell nucleus (apparently to protect the DNA from damage). RNA are just like the DNA, except that there is a small difference in the sugar found in the backbone and also in one of the bases. This bit of the DNA is copied onto a form of RNA called 'messenger' or mRNA, in a process similar to DNA replication. The mRNA then fixes on to the ribosomes in the fluid outside the nucleus of the cell. The point of the RNA which 'fixes' is where the 'AUG' codon, or the 'start' codon is found. The RNA does not 'know' how to find its way about, it just attaches when, in random motion within the cell, the right parts of the RNA and the ribosomes come into proximity, and they 'dock' in a position where they fit, like a lock and key. It is somewhat like a golf ball wandering about a golf course and falling into the hole when it moves over it.

When the RNA molecule is in position like this, another class of RNA called the 'transfer' or tRNA attaches individual amino acids to the succession of codons. The tRNA are specific to each amino acid and the first one to attach to the RNA is the one that has the complement of the AUG 'start' codon. The cell contains enzymes that are chemically the correct 'fit' to help a particular tRNA transfer amino acids to the mRNA. Once the first amino acid is in position, the tRNA carrying the amino acid coded by the next codon moves in to place the next amino acid in position. The two adjacent amino acids then form a chemical bond, the start of a chain of amino acids that goes on to form the protein.

This process continues till the 'stop' codon is reached. Here, enzymes get active and the mRNA is released from the protein that has been synthesized.

This understanding of the sequence of events came in steps, with experiments to deduce what was happening down at the molecular level. Nirenberg and Heinrich Matthaei first developed a way to create simple proteins in a test tube, using mRNA that had been extracted from cells. Khorana carried forward Nirenberg's work with the synthesis of RNA, which in turn could build proteins. Holley followed up with work on the mechanism of transport of mRNAs and the synthesis.

The first RNA synthesized was a chain of only 'U's (the RNA equivalent of 'T' in DNA). This was found to code for a protein that was a chain of the amino acid, phenyl anilinine. We can see from the genetic code chart that UUU codes for this amino acid. Repeating a sequence of 'CA' in the RNA led to the histidine-threonine chain, and so on.

Individual components of the codons had to be identified through carefully designed experiments. For instance, for a particular element appearing in one of the groups, a radioactive form could be used. Now, after breaking up the strand of DNA, that particular strand could be traced by the radioactive 'trail'. Painstakingly using methods like this, the meaning of each codon was worked out and nature's secret code was pieced together. The concise and stable formula for individuals of species to develop, as an expression of the proteins their cells produced, was discovered.

Khorana did the bulk of this work himself and finally completed the decoding: the identification of the proteins that each of the sixty-four codons represented. Along the way, Khorana developed techniques of locating, navigating and marking spots in the DNA, cutting and splicing threads of DNA, the enzymes that could do these things, the way to work with them. These were the forceps and scalpels of dissecting and assembling the fundamental components of genetics.

In just a few years the scientific community realized the importance of the work that had been done. The human genome, or the entire code in the twenty-three chromosomes consists of nearly three billion genes. A handful had been identified, as being involved in specific human ailments. Khorana's techniques led to an industry of generating the specific genetic scraps to help an individual lacking those specific genes to recover lost function. But soon, the community and industry realized the immense potential of mapping the entire human genome. The task was too large for an individual. Biophysicists, microbiologists, information technology experts the world over were drafted in the global Human Genome Project.

The human genome now stands mapped, both by a public group as well as a private enterprise. Humankind now has the most basic blueprint of its nature. Human cells, in principle, can be programmed to eliminate disease or the tendency to disease. There is the possibility of creating super race; there are fears of misuse. Applications in law and crime detection are commonplace. There are fears of invasion of privacy.

The understanding of the mystery of heredity, hesitantly probed 150 years ago, may be the most important part of human knowledge in the twenty-first century.

Khorana is today a naturalized citizen of the US. He is married to Esther Elizabeth Sibler, and has three children. From 1970, he has been a professor at the Massachusetts Institute of Technology, where he has continued to make major contributions to molecular biology. Along with Holly and Nirenberg, he won the 1968 Nobel Prize for medicine.

E.C. GEORGE SUDARSHAN

ABOUT A HUNDRED YEARS AGO physics made great progress in understanding the world as perceptible to human senses—planets, stars, gases, heat and sound. In the beginning of the twentieth century, the focus was on the invisible, atom-scale world, on the atomic structure and spectra, semiconductors and so on. But the latter part of the century was the age of the subatomic. An unexpected variety of entities were discovered which were not a part of the atom, but arose within interactions in the atomic world. These entities hardly existed long enough to be detected or even evaded detection by not interacting at all.

It was in the exciting voyage of discovery through this unknown world that E.C. George Sudarshan of Kottayam, Kerala, made a course-setting discovery while still a graduate student at the University of Rochester, USA.

The achievements of physics till the end of the nineteenth century were milestones along the path of using patterns in the visible world to uncover the principles and laws that seemed to govern material things. Towards the end of the nineteenth century, glimpses into the atomic world showed that the concepts had to be refined to fit new phenomena. The earlier science of forces and its effects, which had worked so well with heavenly bodies, machines and even the molecules of gases, had to make way for quantum mechanics, the new way to calculate the outcome of interactions between very small objects, of the size of atoms. At this scale, the energy of a system, it was found, did not change smoothly, like an airplane taking off, but in steps, or quanta, more like an ostrich leaping faster and faster to launch into flight. These steps were noticeable and important in the world of things subatomic, but merged and disappeared in the world of larger objects.

But even the new methods of quantum mechanics, which worked well for atoms and chemical reactions, fell short when new phenomena multiplied, even in the subatomic world, and theorists had to tack and trim the sails by the hour! This was where George Sudarshan made that fundamental and important discovery to help understand the subatomic world: radioactive decay or 'beta decay'.

Sudarshan was born in 1931 in Kottayam, Kerala. He completed his B.Sc. with honours in physics from Madras Christian College, Chennai, in 1951. He completed his MSc. the following year and shifted to the Tata Institute of Fundamental Research (TIFR), Mumbai. At TIFR, where his colleagues were some of the leading men of science, including Homi Bhabha. He worked on cosmic rays, an area where high-energy radiation from outer space was revealing astonishing new results. During the years at TIFR, Sudarshan also came into contact with George Marshak, with whom he was to do memorable work a few years later.

At the beginning of the twentieth century, the atom was seen to be constituted of just three particles: the positively charged proton, the negatively charged electron, and the neutron, a neutral particle. Another particle known was the photon, the particle of light. The nucleus of the atom was known to consist of protons and neutrons, bound together by a short-range,

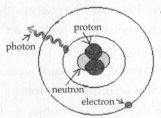

attractive force. Around the nucleus, which is positive because of the presence of protons, the electrons orbit in 'shells' that have successively increasing levels of energy. When the electrons transit from one energy level to another, they absorb or emit photons of the correct energy that separates the levels.

Just these four 'elementary' particles participate in all radioactive decay of nuclei. Three kinds of decay are known. When groups of two protons and two neutrons—which constitute the nucleus of the helium atom—escape from a heavy nucleus, we have what is called alpha decay. Another form of radioactive decay is the emission of high-energy photons, the gamma rays, when the nucleus goes from a higher energy level to a lower level. The third form of decay, known as beta decay, happens when a neutron gets converted into a proton with the emission of an electron to conserve the charge.

Alpha decay was readily explained, as being likely when nuclei were not strongly bound and could allow a stable unit to escape. The protons in the nucleus are positively charged, and they repel each other. As the particles have been brought together against the forces of repulsion, this would have cost some energy. When squeezed close enough together, attractive 'strong' force becomes active and then keeps them together, the way a golf hole at the top of a hill keeps the golf ball safely inside once the ball has been sent all the way up the hill.

In quantum mechanics, there is always a probability of the golf ball popping out of the hole and then rolling down the hill, with a temporary violation of the common laws of physics. In the case of a large nucleus, some of the nucleons are pretty far apart and the attraction is not always that strong. This is like saying the golf hole is not that deep. Hence, particles do escape from the nucleus in groups of four, as alpha decay. The theory of what nuclei will have what rate of alpha decay is then not very complex to compute.

The emission of gamma rays, which are photons, is also fairly straightforward. It arises from energy differences when the nucleus relaxes from a higher energy level, like after alpha decay, which sometimes leaves the daughter nucleus in an 'excited' state.

But the case of beta decay was not so simple. For one thing, it involved the transformation of what was considered to be an 'elementary' particle into another form. But a greater problem was that the energy of the emitted electron was not what it logically should have been. Given the known energies of the neutron at the start and the proton at the end, the electron should have carried away exactly the energy difference. But what was observed was that the electron emerged with a range of energies, including very low amounts. This did not make sense at all.

The Austrian-born Wolfgang Pauli first suggested that the reason may be that there was one more, mysterious, elusive particle being emitted, which took away some of the energy. Enrico Fermi later developed a quantum mechanical theory where he actually showed that there should be a neutral particle with very low mass, christened the 'neutrino', emitted along with beta decay. The neutrino, in fact, was discovered years later to confirm the Fermi theory and became one more of a veritable menagerie of particles that were discovered over the years.

New particles had been discovered in the studies of cosmic rays and cosmic ray 'showers'. Cosmic rays are mostly high-energy electrons that stream in from outer space. These usually interact with the upper atmosphere and very rarely reach the surface of the earth. But in the course of interacting with the atmosphere, they give rise to 'secondaries', which do reach the earth's surface.

One frequent reaction is that a gamma particle, a high-energy photon, spontaneously splits into an electron-positron (e-p) pair. The positron is a particle exactly like the electron, except that its charge is positive. The positron is the 'antiparticle' of the electron, and while the pair arises from a photon, if they meet, they annihilate and give off a photon.

While coursing through the atmosphere, the electron and positron meet up with other positrons and electrons, forming new photons. If these photons had sufficient energy, they could give rise to more e-p pairs and so on.

The photon, electron and positron were detected by the trails they left in bubble chambers. These were large cavities that contained a vapour which condensed around any energetic particles, like electrons, that may pass through the chamber. As the electron and positron were charged particles, their motion would be affected by a magnetic field, in the way a wire carrying a current would be affected. If a magnetic field were placed around the bubble chamber, the electron or positron would thus move in curved paths, leaving trails that curved in different ways and the particles could be identified. Similarly, an electric field would also deflect the charged particles. These measurements also helped find the mass of the particles.

Apart from electrons and positrons, cosmic rays gave rise to a number of other particles, like mesons (or intermediate mass particles) of nine different kinds and hyperons of six kinds. Soon many other particles were discovered, both in cosmic rays and when cosmic rays or the products of radioactivity were made to strike targets of various materials. The subatomic zoo soon became well populated and schemes to classify elementary particles took on the aspects of taxonomy!

In Fermi's explanation of beta decay using the methods of quantum mechanics, the special features of matter at very small dimensions were taken into account. One of these is that particles begin to behave like waves. It is this 'wave' nature that leads to 'quantum' effects, rather like the wave nature of sound leads to resonance. Or like a stretched string vibrates with a 'natural' pitch.

In making quantum mechanical calculations, there is a way of representing things that have mass so that their wave character is reflected. The energy of the system is then the main player, which works on the state of the system and how the system would evolve can be mathematically computed.

When dealing with interactions of particles, problems are solved by combining a mathematical term representing the energy of the system with the mathematical expression representing the state of the system. In case of interactions that we really do not understand, some assumptions are made. The results of the mathematical computation are checked with the outcome of experiments. When we examine the difference between theory and experiment, we can refine the assumptions and progress towards better understanding of the interaction.

In this way, the theory of beta decay had been developed as a form of the 'weak' interaction, one of the four kinds of interactions seen in nature. The first kind, which quantum theory has not treated, is gravity, which is so weak that it is appreciable only between very large and heavy objects, like planets and stars. The next is electromagnetism, which attracts or repels charged objects and which keeps atoms and molecules together.

Gravity and the electromagnetic force have infinite range. The third and fourth kinds are very short-range forces found inside atomic nuclei. The 'strong' force holds protons and neutrons together in the nucleus and is responsible for some kinds of radioactivity. But the last, the 'weak' force, is of the shortest range and is the one that leads to beta decay. It is called 'weak' because of its short range and because beta decay occurs more slowly than alpha decay, which is caused by the 'strong' force.

In developing his theory of the weak interaction, Fermi introduced a term in the energy expression. For consistency with experiment, the term taken for the interaction needed to be of the correct form, in respect of its properties of direction, orientation and so on. Fermi, in developing the theory of beta decay, had just considered the form that had previously worked for the photon. For some time, the Fermi theory was successful.

But then came observations of beta decay in nuclei that had a quality called 'spin'. In a refined theory where this feature was included, the interaction needed to be of yet another kind, in respect to its orientation. But experiment seemed to support a third kind. Further experiment and theory showed yet another pair of possibilities. Studies also showed further methods of orientation as being correct. But the experiments themselves were not always reliable and evidence was not clinching. In 1953, Petschek and Marshak (soon Sudarshan's guide) came to another set of conclusions, a theory that was current till it too was found to fall short. It seemed as if weak interaction was really territory that could not be satisfactorily explained!

It was about this time (1956) that two Chinese scientists Tsung Dao Lee and Chen Ning Yang drew attention to an assumption implicit in the work on weak interactions: that the interactions should conserve a property known as 'parity'. This assumption, they said, may not be justified. Conservation of parity means that the laws of nature should not depend on whether we were left-handed or right-handed. Another way of putting it is that the world should work in exactly the same way even when seen through a mirror. This seems to be a natural condition and it does not look like there could be anything wrong with a theory which assumes that parity would be conserved.

Conservation of parity, in fact, had been basic to the universality of physical laws—that physics should be no different here than on a planet many light years away and with which we could not exchange the meaning of right and left.

But the irony was that Yang and Lee did not find real evidence that beta decay conserved parity and they proposed an experiment to make sure. The experiment was the beta decay of the cobalt nucleus. The cobalt nucleus has a property called spin, which marks it with a direction, like the North Pole on the earth.

A bunch of such nuclei could be oriented with spins in the same direction. The rate of beta decay could then be checked. Only if the rate was the same both in the direction of spin as well as in the opposite direction could parity be conserved.

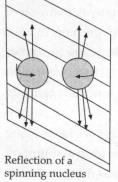

Reflection of a spinning nucleus

On being seen through a mirror, directions of motion and position get reversed. In the case of a spinning nucleus, the direction of spin is reversed. But if rate of decay is different in different directions, which it is, the mirror world is distinguishable from the 'real' world!

At the time of Yang and Lee's work,

Sudarshan was a graduate student at Rochester, USA, working with Professor Marshak. His work was in the field of 'elementary' particles, symmetries and computation of their masses and other properties. The suggestion that weak interactions may not conserve parity had just broken and experiment had shown that this indeed was the case. Sudarshan went hard to work and concluded, first, that there was no form of interaction consistent with the data. Some of the data, hence, had to be wrong. Second, to account for 'spin', the form of interaction needed to include a component that would not change in step with a reflection in a mirror. The momentum of a spinning top has such a property.

In a spinning top, the momentum of the top is taken to be along the axis, and in a given direction, according to the 'right-hand rule'. If the top is then seen reflected in a mirror, the direction of spin clearly gets reversed. But the 'right-hand rule' also gets reversed, into a 'left-hand' rule. The direction of the angular momentum hence remains the same, upwards. This is the property of quantities like angular momentum, to remain unchanged on reflection.

Marshak and Sudarshan, in the term for the interaction, put in a component that was like a quantity with direction, like speed, which was necessary. They also added a small component that was like spin momentum. As the spin momentum term would not change on reflection, there was a part of the interaction that would not change direction along with the others. This addition made sure that parity was violated. With this refinement in place, Marshak and Sudarshan reworked the equations and fixed the values so that results agreed with observations. And by 1957, they had the universal form of the interaction for the weak force, consistent with experiment, ready to present to the world.

What followed could perhaps be viewed as not the best way to bring the fine work that had been done to the attention of the world. The work had been done by the time of the Rochester Conference, in 1957. But Sudarshan, as a graduate student, did not get to present the work and had to hear distinguished speakers puzzle over a problem that he had solved! A little later, Sudarshan presented to a gathering, including the celebrated physicist Murrey Gell-Mann, evidence of how some of the experimental data was inconsistent and their own resolution of the puzzle. Sudarshan and Marshak suggested that some of the experiments be redone. This led to some of the experiments being proved faulty and vindication of the Marshak-Sudarshan form as correct theory. In September 1957, Marshak presented a paper at a conference in Padua-Venice and they considered their finding as good as published. This, in retrospect, was an error. Sudarshan did try to ask Marshak to get the work formally published, but he was then a student, and Marshak appears to have been preoccupied.

A little after Marshak and Sudarshan's work, Richard Feynman and Gell-Mann who had worked on weak interactions from another viewpoint in quantum mechanics, also proposed the same form of interaction for beta decay, in a paper in *Physical Review*. A paper in *Physical Review* was certainly a more public presentation and it is not surprising that for some years it was Feynman and Gell-Mann who were in the limelight for the theory of the weak force.

In the last forty years, the theory of elementary particles has got greatly refined. The proton itself came to be considered to be made of three of a set of particles called quarks, which give rise to the strong force by exchange of gluons. The weak force is seen to arise from exchange of very heavy 'W' particles. In perspective, Sudarshan's early work leading to the form of interaction being responsible for the weak force has been seen as the start of much of the development and now, at least, his place in the story is unquestioned.

Sudarshan got his Ph.D shortly after and he moved on to work at Harvard, Rochester, Berne, Syracuse and from 1969, at the University of Texas at Austin. For eleven years he was senior professor at the Indian Institute of Science, Bangalore, and for six years, director of the Institute for Mathematical Sciences, Chennai. He continued to work in different fields and published several books, including one on particle physics along with Professor Marshak.

JAYANT NARLIKAR

THERE IS PERHAPS NOTHING THAT HAS fascinated humankind for so long as the nature of the cosmos, the pattern behind the sun and the stars. Over centuries of contemplation through long nights undisturbed by city lights, the ancients saw people, animals and gods in the heavens and wove theories and fables around them, the first cosmologies.

It was natural to think of the earth as the centre of the action. The Ptolemaic system traced the movement of the sun and stars as circles around the earth and the paths of the planets as circles within circles. The method was quite accurate in predicting the position of planets and seasons and there was little reason, astronomical or philosophical, to doubt the model.

That the earth could be going around the sun became a serious possibility only after the discovery of the telescope and Galileo's discovery of the moons of Saturn. And yet, for many years, the old system continued to be used in predicting the paths of the planets.

But after the discovery of the telescope and the formulation of Newton's laws of gravitation and motion, much more data about the night sky became available. The solar system was studied in detail and the nature and distribution of the fainter, 'stellar' heavens were analysed. The great bulk of stars were found to lie along a bright belt in the sky, called the Milky Way. This, we now understand, is because the earth is on the outside of a disk-shaped collection of stars, or galaxy. When we look along the plane of the disk, we see the vast number of stars that belong to the galaxy.

The Milky Way is known to be a galaxy because there are methods of measuring the distance to a star and it is found that this multitude of stars lie together, in a collection, while other stars are many times more distant. Painstaking plotting of the positions of stars shows that our galaxy has a bulge in the middle, which may happen if the galaxy were spinning round. And meticulous measurements of the motion of the stars in the Milky Way also corroborates this.

Distant stars were found to consist of groups of stars, or galaxies in their own right. Groups of galaxies were found to form clusters, and groups of clusters to form greater clusters. The scale of distance was in millions of light years, or the distance light travels in millions of years. Travelling at 3,00,000 kilometres a second, light takes about a second to reach us from the moon, some eight minutes to come from the sun, and about five hours for the distance from Pluto. In comparison, Proxima Centauri, our nearest star after the sun, is 4.3 light years away and the Milky Way is 1,00,000 light years across. The farthest stars are over ten billion light years away and this serves as an estimate of the age of the universe itself.

The last century was rich in theorizing about the dynamics of this vast universe. How did the different parts affect each other? What were the processes going on? How far did the universe extend? In the time scale of millions of years, was the universe changeless or turbulent? Physics and mathematics revealed much about the birth, flourishing and death of stars, the nuclear fires that warmed and lit them, and the mysteries of supernovae, neutron stars and black holes.

An astonishing discovery was that the universe appears to be expanding, with the farthest parts receding the fastest! Distances to star clusters were estimated with the help of Cepheids, or stars which regularly wax and wane, over a 'cycle of brightness'. This is the intrinsic brightness, or how it looks before the brightness dims due to distance. It is found that the cycle is slowest with the brightest stars. This rule helps guess the distance to an unknown Cepheid. By measuring the time for one cycle of brightness, we can tell its intrinsic brightness. Then, measuring its apparent brightness reveals how far away it is, which is also the distance to the cluster in which it is found. Using this method, the distance to various stars can be worked out. At what speed the star is receding from us is then calculated with the help of its 'spectral shift'.

The spectrum of light from stars contains special bright or dark lines of light from common elements, like hydrogen, in the atmosphere of the stars. If the star is moving away from the observer, the position of these 'marked' lines shift towards the red side of the spectrum, just like the whistle of a railway engine moving away from us gets less shrill. By measuring how far the lines have 'shifted', we can estimate the speed of recession.

Using these two measuring rods, Edwin Hubble, in 1929, was able to show that all distant stars were receding, and the speed of recession increased as the star went further away. The Hubble rule is now used to measure the distance to the most faraway stars. But more important is the discovery that the universe itself is expanding.

Modern cosmology started in the early twentieth century, which saw two revolutions in scientific thought. These were the quantum theory and the theory of relativity. The quantum theory explained many processes that we believe are taking place in the sun and the stars, while the theory of relativity gave the correct rules to work out the motion of stars and galaxies.

The theory of relativity had its origin in a surprising discovery about the speed of light. Our usual experience is that if we are in a car moving at 100 kmph and we throw a stone backwards at 60 kmph, the stone will strike the ground at 100 − 60 = 40 kmph. But if a beam of light were shone from a speeding meteor, this speed would be the same both when measured from the meteor as well as from the ground!

Einstein showed that the difference arose because our usual measures of distance and time did not stay unchanged when speeds, like that of meteor, approached the speed of light. Einstein showed that from a fast moving point of reference, distances seem to contract and time intervals seem to expand.

Hence, it did not make a lot of sense to think of an event as having occurred at a place, and at a certain time, as neither the place nor the time may be the same for another observer. Einstein replaced the usual three dimensions of space and an independent dimension of time with four dimensions of space and time, in a new space called space-time, where time was interconnected with position. Calculations in this new framework automatically took care of differences in the time and space intervals measured by moving observers.

Einstein then extended the theory by including the effect of gravity. As acceleration due to a force could not be distinguished from the effect of gravity, Einstein considered that gravity and acceleration were the same thing. With this basis, he rewrote the equations of motion in terms of the four-dimensional thinking. Another consequence of the theory of relativity is that energy and mass are equivalent, as demonstrated by the famous equation $E = mc^2$. In the new equations of motion, Einstein expressed masses as energies. Gravity thus arose from energies and was indistinguishable from acceleration. Much of the interaction between masses now reduced to 'geometric' properties of the four-dimensional space. A remarkable thing about this representation was that the presence of a mass got translated into a curve in the four-dimensional space. This would affect the motion of things, like planets, without having to explicitly talk about gravity.

This new view, the General Theory of Relativity, was soon verified with incredible accuracy, in explaining the eccentric motion of Pluto, something that had defied Newtonian mechanics. That mass caused space to curve was also verified when starlight was seen to bend when passing the sun during a solar eclipse.

Einstein then applied his new equations to analyse the dynamics of the universe. As a first simplification, the suns and galaxies were not considered individually, but only 'on the average', as if the total mass of the universe were evenly spread, without 'lumpiness'. Another assumption he made was that the universe was essentially static, which is to say, not evolving or changing in any basic way.

But the approach did not lead to solutions that were completely satisfactory. The only way the universe would not collapse to a point was if it contained a form of matter that had the opposite of gravity—repulsion, with the force increasing with distance.

Alexander Friedmann suggested that these problems arose because the universe was treated as static. If this condition were removed, the theory seemed to work. This seemed to be the answer—to consider the universe not as static, but expanding! Even Einstein granted that 'he had been a fool(!)' to think otherwise!

This was the start of the theories of the expanding universe.

The equations of Einstein were not in three dimensions, like the space we are used to, but were in 'space-time'. The expansion, then, was not the kind that we can visualize, in three dimensions, like an expanding balloon, but was an expansion of space itself. The example of the balloon can illustrate the expansion of space in two dimensions. Take any two points on the balloon. As the balloon expands, the distance between the two points would increase. A two-dimensional being on the surface of the balloon would then experience an 'expanding' of space. If the being were spotting stars in a two-dimensional sky, it would detect the recession of galaxies!

The image of an expanding universe implies that in the past the universe was smaller and at some time it must have been of zero dimension. In the 1940s, George Gamov proposed that the universe may have set out as a primeval atom that suddenly exploded, with tremendous density and heat, and simultaneously become the origin of all matter and space. As this infernal entity expanded, with particles and energy moving outwards, it would pass through stages of being just photons, free electrons and then, neutral hydrogen atoms. And thus, over millions of years, the hydrogen clouds spread out into space, forming the stars and galaxies as we have today.

The theory has now been greatly refined and has passed many tests and has been able to account for many things about the universe. But at the time, it sounded so fantastic, that the renowned astrophysicist Sir Fred Hoyle mockingly dubbed the theory the 'Big Bang', a name that has stuck.

One of the problems with the theory at the time was that it put the age of the universe at around two billion years. This was far short of even geological evidence on the earth, of four to five billion years, and it was known that some galaxies were over ten billion years old. The figure now computed by the big bang theory is in much better agreement, but in the 1940s, this was a serious snag.

Gamov had also proposed that the early universe, being intensely hot, would have emitted radiation like any hot body. Gamov said that some traces of this emission should exist, in the form of uniform background radiation. Though the big bang theory successfully explains many observed cosmological features and is universally accepted as a theory of the origin of the universe, a 'rival' theory—the 'steady state'—also had its adherents as in the 1940s no such radiation had been detected.

In 1948, Fred Hoyle, with Herman Bondi and Thomas Gold, proposed this alternate theory. The theories till then had been based on a 'cosmological principle', that the universe was homogenous and the same in all directions. Hoyle et al suggested going one step further, that the universe was also the same at all times, or in a steady state.

This is not to say that the there are no processes in the universe. By all means, stars would be born, collapse to cores of fiendish temperatures, synthesize the elements, explode as supernovae, crush into black holes . . . but the totality of the heavens would remain unchanged. Somewhat like a street scene which remains much the same through the afternoon, though hundreds come and go!

But how does the expansion of the universe, the receding of the farthest stars, at which point fit into the steady state? If the stars continued to recede beyond some 10,000 million light years, when they would start receding at the speed of light, and disappear from view? Hoyle, Bondi and Gold said that this would be compensated by spontaneous 'creation' of matter everywhere in the universe. Would this not violate the principle of conservation of matter, that matter could neither be destroyed, nor created? And if matter were being continuously created, would we not have seen evidence of the fact?

The objections were countered by evidence of spontaneous creation of matter by gamma rays and other phenomena that allow violations of conservation, in small quantities. In any case, the theory does not attempt to describe the process of creation. It simply says that such creation could be taking place. As for evidence, the universe consists of such vast spaces of near vacuum that the amount of matter, that needs to be created, to make up for the matter that recedes from view, comes to just one atom of hydrogen per litre of space every billion years! Surely, we do not have the capability to measure anything as meagre as that!

The stand taken, in fact, is not as arbitrary as it seems if we consider the possible hypotheses about matter in the universe:

   i. that all matter has always existed.

   ii. that all matter was created at some definite time, the moment of creation.

   iii. that matter is being continuously created.

The first possibility implies that infinite time has elapsed since matter was created. If this be the case, all free hydrogen in the universe would have formed stars and got converted to helium, lithium and the higher elements. But there is still so much hydrogen in the universe that this possibility gets ruled out.

The second possibility is essentially the big bang theory. At the time the steady state was proposed, the big bang had serious flaws.

The third possibility, the steady state, was hence a totally reasonable alternative. But still the steady state theory was pilloried and battered, mainly because it relied not on observation or deduction but leaned on the 'perfect cosmological principle'. Was this not like the Ptolemaic reliance on the 'perfection' of the circle to justify a picture of the cosmos?

This was when Jayant V. Narlikar, a young research scholar at Cambridge became a participant in the debate and collaborated with Hoyle to develop a rigorous basis for the steady state theory. Narlikar, till recently director of the Inter-University Centre for Astronomy and Astrophysics at Pune, has been an important participant in the work done in the last few decades in this field and is one of the leading architects and proponents of the 'steady state' theory.

In the early 1960s, when the big bang was not considered a 'foregone thing', as some view it today, Narlikar was a big name in the field for his work in formalizing the steady state theory. Recent discoveries of previously unknown forms of matter in the universe, including an astonishing kind that experiences gravitational 'repulsion' instead of 'attraction', may even draw the 'steady state' theory nearer centrestage.

Narlikar was born in Kolhapur, Maharashtra, in 1938 and was educated at the Benaras Hindu University. He continued his studies in mathematics and astronomy at Fitzwilliam House, Cambridge, where he took a distinction in the mathematical Tripos and won the Tyson medal in astronomy. He was the W.A. Meak research scholar, selected by Sir Fred Hoyle, in 1960. Subsequently, he went on to win the coveted Smith's prize, and then the Adam prize.

Narlikar and Hoyle developed an efficient theory for the

continuous creation of matter in the setting of Einstein's General Relativity Theory. Historically, what Newton's theory of gravitation did was to link two bodies 'at a distance', with no apparent connection between them. Einstein had replaced this 'action at a distance' with the idea of a 'field' and the force of gravity being due to the structure of space-time. This was so successful that attempts were made to connect electromagnetic and nuclear forces as well with such a geometric approach. These, unfortunately, just made no headway. In the mean time, even electromagnetism, the showpiece of the 'field' approach had been elegantly formulated through the 'particle' approach.

Hoyle and Narlikar now attempted a new theory of gravitation to support the creation hypothesis. The insight of relativity also clears the 'action at a distance' objection by showing that distance itself shrinks to 'no distance', when things move at the speed of light in the four-dimensional space-time continuum. With the 'action at a distance' difficulty out of the way, Hoyle and Narlikar introduced the idea that mass and inertia of matter was not an intrinsic property but arose from interaction with distant bodies. In fact, they developed an equation that relates the mass of any object with the total mass of the observable universe. The equation also implies the creation of new matter quite naturally, and not by the ad hoc insertion of new terms, like Hoyle had done earlier. The theory, in fact, uses the energy of the universe's expansion itself to create the new matter!

Around the same time, independent researchers stumbled upon a uniform microwave radiation background in all space. This was the clear proof of the big bang theory, which had not been there so far. It was a momentous discovery and so revived the big bang school that the steady state hypothesis began to sound like heresy. The 'age of the universe' problem with the big bang theory had also been resolved and now the raison d'être of an alternate theory evaporated.

The steady state theory also suffered the disadvantage of not having made any specific assertion that could be established by experiment. Furthermore, the time, the background microwave radiation had no explanation in the steady state theory at the time. For all its intellectual validity and its contribution to objectivity in science, the steady state theory began to be viewed as a pursuit of academic interest at best.

But Hoyle and Narlikar persisted and soon came out with a modified steady state theory, which permitted 'mini bangs' in localized 'bubbles' where the universe may expand and contract without creation. While the explanation has been viewed as 'contrived', Hoyle and Narlikar, and Narlikar with others, have persisted with revisions and alternates. Thus, Narlikar has played an invaluable role in keeping alive a line of research in the face of widely accepted confirmations of a theory which still bristles with problems. This is all the more important in a field, where, as one thinker said, we are like the fruit fly, which, based on a glimpse of humans during its brief hours of life, is trying to work out the nature of human genetics!

Narlikar went on be elected fellow of King's College and then worked as a staffer in the Institute of Theoretical Astrophysics at Cambridge. In 1972, he returned to India and managed the Theoretical Group for Astrophysics at the Tata Institute of Fundamental Research, Mumbai.

Apart from research, Narilkar has established a name in popularizing science through his writings in English, Hindi and Marathi, and various programmes in the electronic media. For this, he has received the Indira Gandhi Award of the Indian National Science Academy (1990) and the Kalinga Award of UNESCO (1996). In 1988, he founded the Inter-University Centre for Astronomy and Astrophysics, at Pune. He is married to Mangala Rajwade and they have three daughters.